GRETTIR
THE STRONG

GRETTIR
THE STRONG

Retold by
ROBERT NEWMAN

Illustrated by John Gretzer

THOMAS Y. CROWELL COMPANY

NEW YORK

Designed by Mina Baylis
Manufactured in the United States of America
L.C. Card 68-21608

1 2 3 4 5 6 7 8 9 10

Contents

Foreword

Man has always been a teller of tales. He has told them in every age and in every part of the world. And the tales that he has seemed to like best are those of the adventures and great deeds of heroes. The people of Iceland called such tales sagas, and the sagas differ from most other hero tales in one very important respect. Although we cannot be certain that there was ever a Hercules, a Theseus, or an Achilles, we know that Grettir actually lived. We know where his mountain lair in the west was, and his lonely hut on the heath. We know where he was born, where he died, and where he was finally buried.

In other words, the Icelandic sagas—of which this is one of the most famous—are, on the whole, true accounts of actual happenings. The most reliable sagas agree on all major events and dates, and the names and genealogies of those who played a part in them can be found in the *Landnáma-bók*, the Icelandic equivalent of the Domesday Book, which records the names and holdings of Iceland's settlers and is the foundation of the earliest authentic history of the North.

Iceland is a comparatively small island that lies some six hundred miles west of Norway. It was discovered about A.D. 867 by a Norwegian viking. Until that time, Norway did not truly exist as a nation, in the sense that it did not have a king. Instead, there were a number of jarls, or chieftains, each ruling his own folk and usually at war with his neighbors. One of these jarls, Harald, later known as Harald Fairhair, set out to create a kingdom by conquering all the other chieftains. It was a long struggle, but the turning point came at the great sea battle of Hafrsfjord in 872 where he won a decisive victory. After that, he was Norway's single and undisputed ruler.

Many of the defeated chieftains, however, refused to pledge their allegiance to Harald. They and their followers left Norway, sailing to Scotland, the Orkney, Shetland, and Faroe Islands. From there they continued their war against Harald, making raids on Norway until they were driven still farther away: to almost uninhabited Iceland where there was land enough for all and they need not acknowledge any overlord.

This initial settlement of Iceland took two generations, and when it was over, the island had a population of some fifty thousand. Since there were few communities of any size and most of the settlers lived on steads, or farms, that were widely separated, the family was a very important social unit, and its members were intensely loyal to one another. So, in addition to their independence, one of the chief characteristics of the early Icelanders was their strong family feelings.

Having left Norway because of Harald, the settlers in Iceland would not accept any one man as their ruler and established their own form of republic. One of the oldest customs among the Norsemen was the Thing, a gathering or assembly at which laws were passed and legal cases decided, and those who left Norway took this custom with them to Iceland. Each district had its own chieftain, or *godi*, who—until the coming of Christianity—was a priest as well as a chief. And each district had its own Thing. But in the year 930, the All-Thing was instituted, an assembly that took place in the summer and to which all the free men of Iceland were required to come to settle all public questions.

As a form of government, however, the All-Thing had a fatal weakness. Although law cases were heard there and sentences passed—of fines, outlawry, or banishment—it had no power to enforce its decisions. The Lawman, a legal expert appointed by the Thing, could only express an opinion, not make a binding ruling. And the rulings of the Thing itself, though carrying great weight, could be ignored by any chieftain or individual who was strong enough to defy public opinion. Because they were not always sure they could get the justice they wanted—and because of their pride and fierce family loyalty—the early Icelanders often resorted to private vengeance in the case of slayings or of other real or fancied wrongs. In itself, the killing of an enemy in open combat was not considered either wrong or a crime provided it was announced openly and not kept secret. However, the nearest relatives of the slain man were honor bound to follow up the matter in their turn. This accounts for the bloody feuds that were so frequent in the early history of Iceland, the time when the events described in the Grettir saga took place.

In writing this version of the Grettir saga, I have used two translations: that of Eirík Magnússon and William Morris, published by F. S. Ellis in 1869, and that of George Ainslie Hight, published by J. M. Dent in 1914. The verses, however, are my own.

I would like to take this opportunity to thank Mr. Erik Friis of the American Scandinavian Society for answering many questions for me that ranged from matters of geography to points of Icelandic law and were of great help in writing this book.

Robert Newman

1

Concerning Grettir's Family and His Childhood

THIS is the tale of Grettir, who was in his time the strongest man in Iceland and one of the bravest. He was called an unlucky man. And it is true that his lot was hard and that he was accused of many crimes of which he was innocent. But he lived a hero's life and died a hero's death, undone in the end—not by force of arms—but by witchcraft.

Onund Treefoot was Grettir's great-grandfather. He fought against Harald Fairhair when Harald was taking over the rule of all Norway, and he lost his leg in battle. But though they called him Treefoot after that, because of his wooden leg, he was still a mighty warrior, and there were few with two good legs who could stand against him.

Onund went to Iceland along with many of those who would not bend their knees to King Harald. He was given land in the west of Iceland and married twice. After Onund's death, his youngest son went farther inland and bought land at Bjarg. He built a house there, and it was in this house that Grettir was born.

Grettir's father was Asmund. Like Onund Treefoot, he married twice. By the time Grettir was born, Asmund was well along in years and already had two sons. The oldest, Thorsteinn, had been born in Norway, and when his mother—Asmund's first wife—died, Asmund left the boy with his wife's family and returned to Iceland. There he married Asdis, who had been brought up in the house of an important chieftain, and with whom he had three more sons—Atli, Grettir's older brother, Grettir, and Illugi, his younger brother—and also two daughters named Thordis and Rannveig.

Young Grettir came into the great hall of the house at Bjarg. It was late autumn, and a fire burned on the stone hearth in the center of the hall, the smoke swirling in the draft before it found its way out through the hole in the steeply pitched roof. Asmund, Grettir's father, sat near the fire, and Grettir went over to him.

"You sent for me, Father?" he said.

Asmund looked coldly at him. Grettir was now ten

years old. He was a good-looking boy, red-haired and
freckled. And though he was strong for his age, there
was as yet no sign of the great strength that was to be
his later on. His mother loved him dearly, but there
was not much love between Grettir and his father. For
while Grettir's older brother, Atli, had been obedient
and easy to handle, Grettir was quarrelsome, spoke
little, and feared no one, not even his father.

"I have given you several tasks to do," said Asmund,
"and you have done none of them well. You could not
even mind the geese properly."

"Because it was wretched work," said Grettir, "fit
only for an idiot."

"I minded geese when I was your age," said Asmund.
"Did that make me an idiot?"

Grettir did not answer, but there was a look in his eyes that made Asmund flush angrily.

"You have been idle long enough," he said. "Tomorrow you will begin tending the horses."

"That at least is closer to man's work than taking care of geese," said Grettir.

"You are far from a man yet," said Asmund. "Now listen well to what I tell you. One of my mares is named Keingala, and she is very weatherwise. When she will not graze, it means that a storm is coming and you must bring the horses back to the stable."

"It seems strange to trust such things to a mare," said Grettir.

"I put more trust in her than I do in you," said Asmund. "Do as I say!"

"Yes, Father."

So Grettir tended the horses until after Yuletide when the very cold weather set in. Keingala had a heavy winter coat and did not feel the cold, but Grettir was not used to it, and he felt it keenly. But what he minded most was that, early as he took the horses to pasture, Keingala would not return to the stable before it was dark.

One morning he came into the stable and found that Keingala had eaten, not only her own fodder, but that which had been given to the other horses as well. Now, Grettir thought, it was the time to pay her back for this trick as well as her wandering which kept him so late in the pasture. Jumping on her back, he drew his knife and shaved off her winter coat from shoulder to loins, leaving her back bare. Then he drove her and the other horses out to pasture.

Keingala stood the biting of the cold wind on her bare back until noon; then she ran home to the stable. Grettir drove the other horses home and shut them in. When his father asked him where the horses were and he told him, Asmund said a storm must be at hand.

The night passed, and there was no storm. The next day Grettir drove the horses out to pasture again, and

again Keingala would not stay, but returned to the stable. Since there was still no storm or sign of a storm, Asmund thought this very strange. But Grettir said, " 'Many seem wise who are lacking in wit.' "

The third morning Asmund himself went out to the pasture, and when he saw Keingala, he knew why she would not stay out in the cold. But though he thought this must be Grettir's work, he could not be sure, and Grettir would say nothing about it. After this, things were in a worse state than ever between Grettir and his father, and they remained so.

Grettir now began to grow more rapidly, and though all could see that he was going to be a big man, no one could guess at his strength, for he had not yet been tried at wrestling.

There were at that time many youths in those parts. Among them was one named Audun who lived in the neighboring valley. He was several years older than Grettir and accounted the strongest youth of his age in the North. When Grettir was fourteen, his older brother, Atli, took him with him to play at ball with those in the valley. They were paired off for the games, and Grettir was matched against Audun.

Audun hit the ball so that it went over Grettir's head and bounded away over the ice. Grettir grew angry at this, and fetching the ball, he drove it at Audun's forehead.

"That is not how we play ball here," said Audun.

"But if you would rather play at something else, let us do so." And he struck at Grettir with his bat. Grettir dodged the blow, seized Audun, and they began to wrestle.

Now all could see that Grettir was indeed stronger than they had thought. For they all knew of Audun's strength, and though he was older than Grettir, for a time the two seemed evenly matched. But finally, by his greater skill, Audun threw Grettir and began to deal roughly with him. Atli and the others separated them, but Grettir said they had no need to hold him as, " 'The thrall alone takes vengeance at once; the coward never.' "

The others made peace between Grettir and Audun, reminding them that they were kinsmen, and the games went on. But Grettir did not forget how he had been worsted, and all now knew that he was someone to be reckoned with because of his strength as well as his short temper.

2

The Slaying of Skeggi

THORKELL, an important chieftain, was the foster father of Asmund's wife. The next spring Thorkell
rode over to visit Asmund at Bjarg. Since they were
old friends as well as kinsmen, Asmund received him
with open arms.

Thorkell stayed with Asmund for several days, and
the two men talked much together. Thorkell asked
Asmund what he had to say about his sons, and Asmund told him that Atli would probably turn out well,
but that he was not happy about Grettir.

"It is clear that he is going to be a very strong man,"
he said, "but he is headstrong and quarrelsome."

"That does not bode well, kinsman," said Thorkell.

Then they talked about the Thing that would take
place, as always, that summer and to which all free men
must come to help decide law cases and discuss the

ruling of the land. Asmund said that it was becoming difficult for him to travel and that he could not spare Atli since he was very good at managing the estate.

"What then?" asked Thorkell. "Will you send Grettir in your place?"

Asmund said he thought he would, for Grettir was now fifteen years old and, while he was difficult, he was not without wit and should be able to carry out his duties at the Thing if Thorkell helped him.

"It shall be as you say," said Thorkell.

And so when Thorkell arrived at Bjarg again to ride to the Thing, Grettir rode with him. There were some sixty men in Thorkell's party, and they rode south from Bjarg across the heath. Grettir had never been to the Thing before, and he felt very much a man to be traveling so far and in such company.

They slept that night out in the open, and when they woke in the morning, they found that several of the horses—Grettir's among them—had wandered off. Grettir went searching for his horse, and when he came upon it, he found that it had been rolling, for the saddle was under its belly and the sack with all the food he would need at the Thing was gone.

While he was looking for the sack, he saw a man walking the heath and asked him who he was.

"My name is Skeggi," said the man, "and I am traveling to the Thing with Thorkell. But my horse wandered off, and I have lost my meal sack."

" 'Misfortune is lessened when two are together.' "

said Grettir. "I have lost my provisions also. We will help each other to look for them."

Skeggi was pleased at that, and for a time they went about near one another. Suddenly Skeggi ran off and picked something up. Grettir asked him what he had found.

"My sack," said Skeggi.

"Who says so besides yourself?" said Grettir. "Many a thing is like another. Let me see it."

But Skeggi would not let him see it, and when Grettir took hold of it, he would not let it go.

"You men of Midfjord have strange notions," said Skeggi, "if you think that those who are not as wealthy as you will not hold fast to what is theirs."

"Wealth or degree has naught to do with it," said Grettir. "If the sack is truly yours, let me see it."

"It seems to me that you forget things easily," said Skeggi. "For instance, how Audun worsted you."

"I have not forgotten," said Grettir. "But you shall not do as he did."

With that, Skeggi let go of the sack, and pulling his ax from his belt, he struck at Grettir with it. But Grettir caught it by the handle and wrested it from him. Skeggi seized him, and they struggled together until Grettir finally broke free and struck in his turn. Skeggi fell dead with the ax in his brain, and Grettir threw the meal sack on his horse and rode off to join the others.

When he reached them, they asked if he had seen Skeggi, and he answered with a verse:

> *Yes, I saw him. I saw him die.*
> *And you, on the heath,*
> *Can find where he lies.*
> *He who angers a troll*
> *Must suffer her wrath.*
> *Now, ax in his skull,*
> *Skeggi sprawls in the path.*

Thorkell's men were startled at this, but unbelieving, and said it was impossible that a troll could have slain Skeggi in broad daylight. But Thorkell said, "There is more to this than there seems to be. Tell us what truly happened, Grettir."

Then Grettir told them all that had passed between him and Skeggi, and Thorkell said, "This is an unfortunate happening for both you and me. For Skeggi was a man of good family, and since he was traveling with me, I am responsible for him. I will pay whatever boot is judged proper for his death. But it may be that you will be outlawed, too, and about that I can do nothing. Now, Grettir, will you still ride on with us to the Thing and chance what may occur there, or will you go back home?"

Grettir said he would go on to the Thing, and to the Thing he went. The slaying was taken up by Skeggi's kinsmen, and though Thorkell paid them the compensation that was set, Grettir was in addition declared an outlaw and banished from Iceland for three years.

When Grettir returned home to Bjarg and told his father what had happened, Asmund was very angry. But he said he was not surprised. Grettir had been a troublesome boy, and he had known he would be a troublesome man.

"The slaying was not of my choosing," said Grettir. "I was but defending myself."

"That may be," said Asmund. "But I fear that there is that about you which will always cause violence, and you are not one who will school himself to avoid it."

In this, as in most things, Asmund was right. And with this slaying, when he was but fifteen, began Grettir's long years of outlawry and wandering.

3

The Journey to Norway
and the Adventure of
the Grave Mound

ASMUND knew a sea captain who had a ship of his own. When Asmund learned that he would soon be sailing to Norway, he sent to him and asked him if he would take Grettir with him. The captain answered that he had heard that Grettir was not easy to get along with but that out of friendship for Asmund he would take him.

Grettir then prepared to leave Iceland. But when he came to go, he found that his father was not giving him very much to see him on his way, just the food he would need on the voyage and some *wadmal*, the homespun cloth that the Icelanders often used for trading instead of money.

Grettir asked his father if he would not at least give him a weapon, but Asmund said, "You have never obeyed me. And if I give you a weapon, I fear what use you will put it to. So I will not give you one."

" 'No favor requires no thanks,' " said Grettir, and so they parted with little love between them.

There were many who wished Grettir a good voyage, but few wished him a safe return. Of these few, his mother, Asdis, was one. For in spite of all the difficulties he had caused, she still loved him very much. She went with him along the road, and when it was time to part, she said, "You do not go forth as I would wish, my son. But the worst of it is that you have no weapon, for my heart tells me that you will need one."

Then she took from under her cloak a goodly and well-wrought sword and gave it to him, saying, "This was the sword of Jokull, my father's father, who was among the bravest of the men of Vatnsdal. It won him many victories. May it serve you as well."

"It is easy to see," said Grettir, "that they are right who say, 'Best to son is mother still.' "

He thanked her warmly and said he would treasure it and never dishonor it. Asdis embraced him and gave him her blessing, and he left her and rode south to the coast where the ship was being loaded.

The captain made him welcome, and when the cargo was all aboard, they put to sea. They ran into heavy weather soon after they left port, and the captain said that this was a bad sign and that a voyage that began so badly was likely to end badly. Grettir thought this

sounded like his father and paid no attention to it. But as they drew near the coast of Norway, the weather became even worse, and in the dark of night the ship struck a rock, and those aboard her had barely enough time to go ashore before she sank.

In the morning they saw that they were on a small island and that there was a much larger island nearby. Those who knew that part recognized the larger island as Haramsey, which lies off the west coast of Norway.

The most important landowner on Haramsey was a man named Thorfinn. When word was brought to him that a ship had been wrecked nearby, he at once put out in one of his boats to see if he could be of help. He brought Grettir and the others back to his house. They stayed there for about a week. Then the sea captain and his crew went off on a ship that was sailing south, but Grettir stayed on as Thorfinn's guest.

Since Thorfinn had large holdings, he was very busy about his estate, but Grettir was no more interested in this than he had been in the managing of the estate at home. However he became good friends with a man whose name, like that of the youth with whom he had fought when they were playing ball, was Audun. This Audun lived a few miles from Thorfinn's stead and Grettir went to visit him almost every day.

One evening, as he was about to return to Thorfinn's house, he noticed a mound on a nearby headland that seemed to glow in the failing light.

"If we saw such a thing in Iceland," said Grettir, "we would say there was a treasure buried there."

"If there is a treasure," said Audun, "it is one that had better be left alone."

"Why so?" asked Grettir.

That, Audun told him, was the howe, or grave-mound, of Kar the Old, father of Thorfinn. Once there had been many farmers on Haramsey. But after Kar died, he had not lain quietly in his grave. His ghost had walked and had frightened away all the other farmers, so that now the whole island belonged to Thorfinn.

"You have done well to tell me this," said Grettir. "Have digging tools ready, and we shall look into the matter tomorrow."

Audun told him that Thorfinn would not like this, but Grettir said he would risk his anger.

Grettir returned the next day, and he and Audun went to the howe, climbed to the top, and began digging down. It was dusk before they reached the beams that roofed the inner chamber. Grettir broke through them and let down a rope. Audun begged him not to go into the howe, especially at night, but Grettir told him to watch the rope and slid down it.

It was very dark in the howe, and the air was heavy and not pleasant. Grettir began groping about in the darkness. The first thing he felt were large bones, the bones of a horse that had been slain and put in the howe

with Kar the Old. Then he came upon a throne on
which there seemed to be a man sitting. And before the
throne was a small but heavy chest with a treasure of
gold and silver heaped about it.

   Grettir carried the chest to the rope, and as he put it
down, he felt himself gripped by a strong hand and
knew that the howe dweller was upon him. Now began a fearsome struggle. Back and forth they stag-
gered, knocking over the throne and smashing all that
lay about them. Several times was Grettir forced to his
knees. But finally, putting forth all his strength, Grettir
overthrew the howe dweller, and drawing the sword
of Jokull, he cut off his head and laid it between his

thighs. For this, he knew, was the way to keep a ghost from walking.

Spent and sore, Grettir carried the rest of the treasure to the rope and called to Audun. But, having heard the noise of the struggle and believing Grettir to have been killed, Audun had fled. Grettir climbed the rope, drew the treasure up after him, and carried it to Thorfinn's house.

Thorfinn and all the others were at supper, and Thorfinn looked at Grettir sharply and asked him why he was so late.

"Pressing things may hap at any time, even at dusk," said Grettir, and he laid the treasure he had taken from the howe on the table before Thorfinn.

Thorfinn's eyes widened when he saw it, and he asked Grettir whence it had come, and Grettir told him.

"Light do you make of it," said Thorfinn. "No man before you was so hardy as to break into the howe and face the wrath of him who dwells there. But since I hold it wrong to bury treasure in the earth when living man may use it, and since you have brought it to me, I blame you not. Indeed, I thank you. And I thank you most of all for this"—and he held up a short sword—"for it is an heirloom of my house and much prized."

"And prized it should be," said Grettir, "for it is the fairest weapon I have ever seen. It is the one thing in all the treasure that I misliked giving you."

"Well, as I told you, it is an heirloom," said Thor-finn, "though it never came into my hands. So you would have to perform an even greater deed than conquering the howe dweller before I would give it to you."

"As to that," said Grettir, "that may yet be."

And so Thorfinn kept the sword and the treasure. Then the winter drew in, and the weather became cold and bad for voyaging, and Grettir stayed on with Thorfinn.

4

The Adventure with the Berserks

THE summer before this, just before Grettir came to Haramsey, the Earl Erik of Norway had called together all the important chieftains and landowners of the realm to talk with them about the rule of the kingdom. Thorfinn was a friend of the earl and a wise man, so he was present at the meeting.

There were at that time many pirates and wicked men who traveled about Norway, challenging anyone with wealth to a *holmgang*, or duel. If the man refused to fight, the challenging viking took his money and his women. If he accepted the challenge, he often lost his life as well as all else, and no boot or compensation was paid for his death. All who met with the Earl Erik, and especially Thorfinn, said that something should be done about this. So the Earl Erik abolished this kind of dueling and declared all who disturbed the peace in this way to be outlaws.

Now the two worst and most violent ruffians in Norway were two brothers named Thorir the Paunch and Ogmund the Evil. They came from the north, and they were bigger and stronger than other men. Not only that, but when they were enraged, the berserk fury would come on them, and they would howl and foam at the mouth, and then no one could stand against them. When they heard that they had been declared outlaws, and that Thorfinn had been the man most responsible for this, they decided to take vengeance on him.

Just before Yuletide, Thorfinn left Haramsey to visit a farm of his on the mainland where it was his custom to entertain his friends. His daughter, a girl of about eighteen, was sick, and Thorfinn's wife stayed at home to take care of her. Grettir and eight servingmen stayed at home also.

The day before Yule, Thorfinn's daughter was much better and got up to help her mother with the preparations for the feast. Grettir had been up since dawn, watching the ships sailing by as men went to join their friends for the Yule feasting and drinking. At dusk he saw a ship making for Haramsey. She was not large, but she had shields hanging over her side as if she were sailing to battle. The ship landed at Thorfinn's boathouse, and twelve men came ashore. Grettir did not like their looks, and he thought he could guess who they were.

As the twelve vikings started towards Thorfinn's house, Grettir went up to them and, in a friendly fashion, asked them their names. Their leader said that he was Thorir, called the Paunch, and that the other big man with him was his brother, Ogmund.

"I think," he said, "that your master, Thorfinn, may have heard of us."

"I have heard of you, too," said Grettir. "And I must say that you are a lucky pair. Thorfinn and all his men are away until after Yule. But his wife and daughter are here, so if I had a grudge against him, this is just the time I would pick to pay him back."

"Now was my counsel good or not?" Thorir asked Ogmund. "Not only is Thorfinn away, but this young man is ready to tell us everything we want to know before we even ask it."

"We are each his own master," said Grettir. "Now if you will come to the house, I will see that you are well entertained."

He led them to the house, talking all the while, and brought them into the hall. Thorfinn's wife was there, decorating it for Yule, and Grettir said, "Behold, mistress, we have honored guests come to share our Yuletide feast with us. For here is the great chieftain Thorir the Paunch and his followers."

Thorfinn's wife paled, but she answered bravely, "I call him not a great chieftain, but a great robber and knave. And you are not much better if you treat him and his fellows as friends after all that Thorfinn has done for you!"

"You would be wiser to welcome them and take their wet clothes rather than reproach me," said Grettir. "There will be time for that later."

"Be not angry, mistress," said Thorir. "And regret it not that Thorfinn is away. For I and my men will see to it that neither you nor your women shall be lonely."

"Though they may seem to act otherwise," said Grettir, "I think that they will like that."

The women, all terrified, began to weep and fled the hall.

"Give me your wet clothes and your weapons," said Grettir, "for we shall get little from them while they are frightened."

Thorir said he cared not about the women's tears or

the fears of the servingmen. "But we will not treat you as we will the others," he said, "for you are acting toward us like a true friend."

"I treat each man as he deserves," said Grettir.

When they had laid aside their weapons, Grettir himself began to serve them, bringing them ale from the cellar. They were tired and thirsty, and began to drink a great deal. But much as they drank, Grettir always brought them more ale, and the strongest ale he could find. And all the while he told them merry tales.

"Never have I met a stranger who treated me so well," said Thorir. "Drink fellowship with us, and when we leave here, you shall be part of our band."

"If you still want me when you do leave, I shall be glad to join you," said Grettir. "But it is growing late, and before you go to bed, would you not like to see where Thorfinn keeps his treasure?"

They said they would, so he led them out to the storehouse, which was strongly built and had a lock on the door. The men were now very drunk and began pushing Grettir about in play. He fell down the outside steps as if he were drunk, too. Then, getting to his feet, he slammed the door and locked it. Thorir and his companions paid no attention to this at first, for they had a light with them and were busy examining Thorfinn's treasure.

Now Grettir ran back to the hall and called to

Thorfinn's wife and asked if there were any weapons about.

"There are weapons," she said. "Why do you want them?"

"Because if we are ever to use them, this is the time," said Grettir.

"Now thanks be to God!" said Thorfinn's wife. "There is a spear hanging over Thorfinn's bed. Also a helmet and the short sword you brought from the howe. They will not fail you if your heart does not."

Grettir put on the helmet, took the spear and sword, and went back to the storehouse. The mistress called to her servingmen and told them to help Grettir. Four of them took arms and followed him, but the other four were afraid to.

Meanwhile it came to Thorir and his band that something was wrong. Trying the door and finding it locked, they began to batter upon it till the whole building shook. Then the berserk fury came on them, and they howled like wolves. By main strength they broke open the door, and at that moment Grettir returned. Taking the spear in both hands, he thrust it at Thorir so hard that it passed through him and into the chest of Ogmund, who was behind him, and with that one stroke he killed them both.

Wrenching the spear free, Grettir attacked the others as they came out, sometimes thrusting with the spear, sometimes hewing with the sword. And though

the berserks had no weapons but only such pieces of wood as were lying about, it was still a great feat for Grettir to stand against them, for they were ten and all of great strength, and he was only one and not yet a grown man.

Two more of them Grettir slew before the storehouse; then the servingmen came up. But they did Grettir little good, for when the berserks turned against them, they ran away again, back to the house. Two more of the berserks fell here, slain by Grettir, and the remaining six fled to the boathouse where they defended themselves with oars. One of them dealt Grettir a great blow, almost crippling him, but still Grettir slew him and one of his companions. Now again the four marauders fled, two this way and two that. Grettir followed one pair to a barn, and there, after another long battle, he killed them, too.

The night was now far gone; it was beginning to snow; and Grettir was stiff and weary, so instead of searching for the last two of the berserk band, he went back to Thorfinn's house.

Thorfinn's wife had put a light in the window to guide him, and when he came into the hall, she said, "Now have you earned much glory and saved me and my household from great shame."

"I am the same man I was earlier this evening," said Grettir. "But the words you speak to me now are different from the words you spoke then."

"I knew neither the might that was in you then nor what you meant to do," she said. "Now everything in this house is yours, and when Thorfinn returns home, I am sure he will reward you properly."

Grettir thanked her and said that all he wanted at the moment was rest, and rest he did, though with his weapons at hand. In the morning all the men of the island were called, and Grettir led them in a search for the last two berserks. At day's end they were found on the far side of the island, both dead from the cold and the wounds that Grettir had given them. They were buried near the shore, and when Grettir returned to the hall, he spoke a verse to Thorfinn's wife:

> *We have dug graves where the waves wash*
> *And laid twelve to rest.*
> *No aid had I through dark of night;*
> *My sword alone dealt death.*
> *Now tell me, lady, and tell me sooth;*
> *Of all the deeds by heroes wrought,*
> *Can one be called worthy*
> *If this be deemed naught?*

She said she could think of no deed that was worthier or more likely to be remembered and sat him in the high seat, and he had the best of everything while they waited for Thorfinn's return.

5

Thorfinn's Return
and Grettir's Adventure
with the Bear

WHEN Yuletide was past, Thorfinn sailed home to
Haramsey. As his vessel drew near to the island,
he and his men saw a strange ship pulled up on the
beach, and Thorfinn's face became grim.

"I fear things have happened here," he said, "that I
would give the whole island not to have happened."

His men asked him what he meant.

"That is the ship of Thorir the Paunch and Ogmund," he told them, "the worst men in all Norway.
They will not have dealt gently with us, for who
was there to stay them? Certainly not that Icelander,
Grettir."

With weapons in hand and with heavy hearts, they
started toward the house. But before they could reach

it, Thorfinn's wife and daughter came hurrying to meet them. Thorfinn embraced them both joyfully and said, "Now God be praised that I see you both well! I will not tell you what I feared when I saw that strange ship on the beach."

"There was much to fear," said Thorfinn's wife. "And we would have suffered sorely if it had not been for your winter guest."

She told him what had happened and of Grettir's great deed, and he went with her into the hall where Grettir sat. Thorfinn embraced him and thanked him with the fairest words he knew and said, "I hope the day never comes when you need a friend to back you to the utmost. But if you should need one, know that you have one in me. For I can never repay you for what you did here. Meanwhile, my house is yours."

Grettir thanked him in turn and said his friendship meant much to him. He spent the rest of the winter in Haramsey, and in the spring Thorfinn asked him where he would go and what he would do. Grettir said he would go to the fair at Vagar in the far north, the most famous fair in Norway, and Thorfinn said he would give him as much money as he wanted. But Grettir said he would only take enough to keep him through the summer. So Thorfinn gave him that and also the short sword that Grettir had found in the howe, and Grettir was well pleased and said that the sword would always be his most cherished possession.

When Grettir arrived at Vagar, he had much honor, for everyone had heard of his great deed with the berserks and many there asked him to come and spend the winter with them. But Grettir thought he would return to his friend Thorfinn, and took passage on the ship of an important man named Thorkell. During their voyage south, Thorkell pressed him to stay the winter with him, and Grettir finally agreed.

That winter, among many others, Thorkell had a man named Bjorn staying with him. Bjorn was distantly related to Thorkell and was the captain of his ship. He was a hot-tempered man who thought very well of himself and not much of Grettir, so they did not get on at all.

Early in the winter a great bear left its lair and began ravaging the countryside, killing both men and cattle. Since Thorkell was the richest man in those parts, he suffered most from these attacks, and he called together his men to search for the bear's den. They found it in a cave near the top of a cliff by the sea. The path leading to it was narrow with a sheer drop to the beach on one side and the wall of the cliff on the other.

"Now that we know where he lives," said Bjorn, "we shall see how things go between me and my namesake." For his name, Bjorn, meant bear.

A few nights later Bjorn went alone to the den, thinking to have the glory of killing the bear by himself. He lay down in the path, covering himself with his shield. His plan was to lie there in this way and stab up at the bear as it passed over him. But the bear knew he was there and was in no hurry to come out, and finally Bjorn fell asleep. When the bear did come out, it did not pass over him as Bjorn had expected, but pulled the shield off him so that it fell down the cliff. Awakened suddenly and rudely, Bjorn took to his heels and ran home, narrowly escaping the bear's claws. When Thorkell's guests learned what had happened, they did not spare Bjorn with their jests.

At Yuletide, Thorkell, Grettir, Bjorn, and some others went again to the bear's den. The bear was there, as he always was in the daytime, but he would not come out, and they could not reach him with their spears. Bjorn kept urging them on, but stayed well back out of danger. Finally it began to grow dark, and they made ready to return home. Grettir had been wearing a fur cloak which he had taken off when they were attacking the bear, and when no one was watching, Bjorn threw it into the bear's den. Seeing it in the bear's grip, Grettir said, "Now who has been making game of me?"

"Whoever did it would not be afraid to say so," said Bjorn.

"But it seems he is afraid," said Grettir. "And of other things besides."

They then started down the narrow path. But they had only gone a little way when the thong on Grettir's legging broke, and he told the others to go ahead while he fixed it. When they were gone, Grettir drew his sword, tied it to his wrist, and went back toward the den. When the bear saw but a single man there, he charged from his cave, striking a fierce blow at Grettir. But Grettir smote shrewdly with his sword, cutting

off the beast's paw. Then, as the bear roared and attempted to strike at him with his other paw, Grettir closed with him, holding him off so that the enraged beast could not bite him. So furious was the struggle that both fell from the narrow path to the beach below. But the bear was underneath and was badly hurt, and before he could do more, Grettir ran his sword into his heart.

Thorkell and all the other guests were drinking in the hall when Grettir returned. He was wearing his cloak which the bear had torn to tatters, and at first all laughed at it. But when he laid the bear's paw on the table and told them the beast was dead, they laughed no more.

"Never did your sword bite like that," said Thorkell to Bjorn. "Now I would like you to say something to Grettir to make up for the trick you played on him."

"I have nothing to say to him about that or anything else," said Bjorn.

Thorkell marked how Grettir looked at Bjorn and said, "As your host I ask you, Grettir, that you do nothing more about this while you and Bjorn are both with me."

"You have my word that I will not," said Grettir.

Bjorn said he did not fear Grettir no matter where they might meet. Grettir said nothing more, but his look made it clear that if they did meet again the matter would not end there.

6

The Slaying of Bjorn
and His Brothers

THE meeting between Grettir and Bjorn took place
the following fall. Grettir had spent the spring and
summer traveling about Norway, but during that time
Bjorn was much on his mind. While he was waiting
for a ship to take him to visit his friend Thorfinn at
Haramsey, a vessel that had been trading in England
put into the harbor. Bjorn was her master, and when
he came ashore, Grettir went up to him and said, "Now
that the trading season is over, perhaps we can settle
our affairs."

Bjorn said he did not know what affairs he was
talking about, and Grettir spoke a verse:

Fierce was the bear who lived in the cave.
This is the hand that slew him.
A rascal there was who thought it a jest
To see my cloak torn to tatters.
As Thorkell's guest, I spared you then,
But the time has come to make amends.

Bjorn said he would be willing to pay a fair amount for the cloak and for Grettir's injured feelings, but Grettir said he was not interested in money, that Bjorn had acted toward him with spite and envy, and that this could not be paid for with silver. Seeing that talk would not mend matters, Bjorn drew his sword, and they fought. But they had not exchanged many strokes before Grettir dealt him one that was his death.

After the slaying, Grettir went to Haramsey and told Thorfinn what had happened, and Thorfinn said that he would never forget what Grettir had done in saving his wife and daughter and that he was glad to have a chance to prove his friendship. When Grettir was summoned to appear before the Earl Sveinn, who was then regent of Norway, Thorfinn went with him.

Now there was a brother of Bjorn's named Hjar-randi in the earl's bodyguard, and he asked the earl for his support, so that it seemed as if things would go badly for Grettir. But when the case was looked into, it was found that Bjorn had been at fault in many ways. Thorfinn offered to pay whatever fine the earl thought

proper and also reminded him that Grettir had served
all Norway well by killing the berserks.

The earl agreed that this was a great service and
urged Hjarrandi to accept Thorfinn's offer of compensation. But Hjarrandi said he would not, and left
the meeting. Again men suspected that matters would
not end there, and Thorfinn set one of his kinsmen,
Arnbjorn, to keep watch over Grettir, for he knew
that Hjarrandi was determined to take his life.

A few days later, Grettir and Arnbjorn were walking through the streets of the town when suddenly a man ran out of a gateway and struck at Grettir with an ax. Grettir had not seen the man coming, but Arnbjorn had, and he pushed Grettir aside so hard that he fell to his knees. The ax cut into Grettir's shoulder blade and under his arm, and a great wound it was. But in spite of it, Grettir rose to his feet, and seeing that it was Hjarrandi who had attacked him, he drew his sword and killed him.

When word of this was brought to the earl, he was very angry and summoned Grettir to come before him the next day. Grettir appeared, accompanied by Thorfinn, and the earl charged him with manslaughter. Grettir admitted the killing, but he said it had been done in self-defense, and he showed the wound that Hjarrandi had given him in proof.

There was in the earl's court at that time a man named Bessi who had been a friend of Grettir's in Iceland and had played ball on his side when Grettir had wrestled with Audun who lived in the neighboring valley. Bessi came forward with Thorfinn, and both begged the earl to fine Grettir as he saw fit but to spare his life.

"It is too bad that Hjarrandi's ax did not find its mark," said the earl to Grettir, "for I think that many will still die because of you."

But he finally agreed to withhold judgement on the

case for the time being. Bjorn and Hjarrandi had a brother named Gunnar who lived in the town of Tunsberg, and the earl wanted Gunnar to be present when he gave his judgement on the slaying. So he told Grettir to appear before him in Tunsberg the following spring.

Again Grettir spent the winter with Thorfinn at Haramsey, and in the spring he went to Tunsberg as the earl had ordered. A few days after they arrived, a tall, richly dressed man with a chieftain's bearing came up to Grettir in the street and asked, "Are you Grettir of Bjarg?"

"I am," said Grettir.

"Nay, reach not for your sword," said the man, laughing. "I am a friend and more than a friend. I am Thorsteinn Dromund, the son of your father, Asmund, and his first wife, and therefore your half brother."

"We are well met then," said Grettir, embracing him joyfully. "For the way things stand with me now, I have great need of friends."

"So I have heard," said Thorsteinn. "And that is why I sought you out. For I wanted you to know that in me you have one on whom you can count no matter what happens."

He warned Grettir that Gunnar had just come to Tunsberg and had vowed to have Grettir's life, and he advised Grettir to avoid him if he could. Grettir said he would, and he tried to do so, but it was not easy because whenever he went out into the streets, Gunnar followed him.

One day Grettir was sitting in one of the drinking booths that had been set up in the town when suddenly the door burst open and in rushed Gunnar and three companions. Their swords were already in their hands, and they began a savage assault on Grettir. But Grettir had his arms with him also, and backing into a corner, he defended himself. He slew one of Gunnar's followers, then went over to the attack. Leaping up onto a bench, he cut down over the top of Gunnar's shield, and that was Gunnar's deathblow. Gunnar's remaining men took to their heels and ran straight to the Earl Sveinn and told him what had happened.

Furious, the earl summoned an assembly to judge

the case. When Thorfinn, Thorsteinn, and Bessi heard the news, they called together their friends and followers, and appeared before the earl. The earl was so angry that at first he would listen to no one. But Thorfinn would not be denied, and he said, "I have come to offer whatever compensation you think is proper for the death of Gunnar, but I ask you to spare Grettir's life."

"Never!" said the earl. "He has killed three brothers, one after the other, and for that no one can pay but Grettir, and he must pay with his life."

Then Bessi stepped forward and said, "You accepted blood money for the death of Bjorn. It was because of Bjorn's death that Hjarrandi attacked Grettir, and Grettir had to kill him in self-defense. And now it is the same with Gunnar. When Grettir slew him, he was but defending himself. Grettir is a man of high birth and my good friend. I offer you everything I possess to compensate for this slaying."

"It does you great credit to make such an offer," said the earl. "But I say to you what I said to Thorfinn. For this slaying I will accept no boot."

Now Thorsteinn Dromund came forward, and he, too, offered blood money, and when the earl asked him why he did so, Thorsteinn said, "Because I do not think Grettir is to blame here and because he is my brother."

"I did not know that," said the earl. "And it speaks well for you that you should support him. But I say to you what I said to the others. This time Grettir must pay with his life."

The earl would hear no more talk after this but called up his guard and told them to search out Grettir.

"You will not have to seek for him," said Thorsteinn. "You will find him at my house. And you will find others there, too." And he and Thorfinn and Bessi left the hall.

When the earl and his men came to Thorsteinn's house, they found Grettir standing before it, and with him were Thorsteinn, Thorfinn, Bessi, and all their friends and followers. The earl ordered them to surrender Grettir and not bring trouble on themselves, but this they said they would never do. They spoke fair words to the earl and again offered to pay whatever compensation he set, but they said they would not give up Grettir.

"If he dies, we shall die with him," they said. "And we shall not die alone."

"Then many shall die!" said the earl, and he was about to order his guard to attack when several men of good will went up to him and begged him to stay his hand. They reminded him that those who opposed him were all the bravest of warriors and that it would be a costly thing to fight them. The earl thought about this and finally let himself be persuaded to set a compensation.

"I do this because I do not wish to fight my own

men," he said. "Though it does not seem to trouble you that you would be fighting against me."

"That is not so," said Thorfinn. "It was a hard choice for us, and we honor you greatly for deciding as you did."

Then the earl set the compensation, but he said that Grettir must leave the country on the first ship sailing to Iceland. Thorfinn and the others agreed to this and paid the money, and the earl withdrew his forces. Then Grettir embraced them all and spoke a verse:

> *Staunch at my side stood the stalwarts:*
> *My brother in blood and two more—*
> *Thorstein and Thorfinn and Bessi—*
> *Outfacing the earl and his horde.*
> *Odin's ravens remember their names*
> *As I shall remember their deed,*
> *For their blades blazed bright beside me*
> *In Tunsberg when great was my need.*

Grettir went back north to Haramsey with Thorfinn and stayed with him until they found a ship that was sailing to Iceland. And though Thorfinn knew that what he had done had cost him the earl's favor, he gave Grettir many valuable gifts and told him to come and stay with him again if he should ever return to Norway.

7

Grettir's Return to Iceland and the Horse Fight

IT was summer when Grettir arrived in Iceland. He was now eighteen years old and already famous because of his deeds in Norway. His mother was overjoyed to see him, and Asmund, his father, chose to forget how things had been between them and welcomed him warmly, and so did Grettir's brother Atli.

Shortly after Grettir returned, he heard that there was to be a great horse fight at Langafit. His brother, Atli, had a stallion which was to be matched with one that belonged to a man named Kormak. Kormak's horse was to be handled by one of his kinsmen named Odd, and Grettir offered to handle Atli's horse for him.

"Only if you can keep your temper," said Atli. "For we will be dealing with difficult and overbearing men."

"So much the worse for them," said Grettir.

They rode to the meadow at Langafit, which was next to a river. Grettir and Odd led out their stallions. They each carried a pointed stick with which to goad their horses if it should prove necessary, but it was not, for they were both spirited beasts and at once began to fight, rearing and biting and kicking. Odd stood close to his horse's head, and those watching could not be sure that he was not using his goad to drive Atli's horse away from his own, but Grettir kept his temper and did nothing about this. Still fighting, the horses moved closer to the river, and suddenly Odd stabbed at Grettir with his goad, giving him a painful wound in the shoulder. Then, as the horses reared, Grettir struck back at Odd. He drove at him so hard that he broke three of Odd's ribs, and Odd fell into the river, pulling his horse in with him.

At this, Kormak's men went for their weapons, and so did the men from Bjarg, but all the others there came between them and would not let them fight. Atli was not happy about what had happened, but he did not blame Grettir for it.

A few weeks later Grettir was visiting one of his kinsmen when he heard that Kormak, Odd, and several others were riding in that direction, coming from the south. He immediately set out to meet them, taking two of Atli's men and two other men with him.

They met Kormak and his party on the heath, and all dismounted. Grettir said that free men should not

fight with sticks as they had at Langafit when they
could fight in other ways. Kormak said that this was
so, and a struggle began between them. At first it was
only a rough sort of play, for they fought with their

bare hands and without weapons, but even so men on both sides were hurt, especially those who came up against Grettir.

While they were fighting, up rode another group of men. Their leader was one Thorbjorn known as Oxmain, because he was as strong as an ox. With him was a kinsman also named Thorbjorn but called the Slow —not because he was slow with his weapons or his tongue, for he talked much and liked to stir up trouble—but because wherever he went he arrived late. Also in the party were two men named Gunnar and Thorgeir.

When Thorbjorn Oxmain came up, he told his men to go in between those who were fighting and stop them. They tried to do so, but when Gunnar and Thorgeir came up to Grettir, he knocked them both down. This so enraged Gunnar that he drew his sword and began laying about and killed one of Atli's men. Then all drew their weapons, and the fray would have become truly deadly, but Oxmain shouted, "I tell you again to hold! And I tell you also that I and my men will fight on the side of whichever party obeys me!"

At this, Grettir called off his men, for they would have been greatly outnumbered if Oxmain's party had joined that of Kormak. He was very angry as he rode home to Bjarg, and it did not make his anger less when he heard that Thorbjorn the Slow was boasting about how he and Oxmain had made Grettir withdraw from the fight.

8

The Fight with Glam's Ghost

For the rest of the summer, Grettir was sullen and short of temper, constantly looking for someone with whom he could fight or for some deed that was worth doing.

In the late fall, when winter was approaching, he rode north to visit his mother's brother, Jokull, the grandson of the Jokull whose sword his mother had given him. As he rode through Vatnsdal, it seemed to him that much of the valley was deserted. There were almost no cattle or sheep grazing in the fields, and many of the farmsteads seemed empty.

Jokull welcomed Grettir warmly, and that night when Grettir told him what he had seen during his ride, Jokull said, "It is so. Many have left Vatnsdal because of their fear of Glam's ghost. And if no help is found soon, the whole of the valley may be abandoned."

"Who is this Glam and why does his ghost walk?" asked Grettir. Then Jokull told him the story, and a frightening story it was.

There was a man named Thorhall who lived in a stead in the southernmost part of Vatnsdal. He was a wealthy man with much livestock, but he could not get anyone to tend his beasts for him because those parts were haunted. He spoke to Skapti the Lawman about this, and Skapti said he would send him someone who might do.

"His name is Glam, and he is a Swede," said Skapti. "He is a big, strong man and not easy to get on with. But I do not think he fears anything."

Thorhall said that would suit him well, but when he saw Glam, he was not so sure about it. For Glam was big, as Skapti had said, but he had a wolflike face and great gray eyes and long, gray wolflike hair. Thorhall told him that the place was said to be haunted, but Glam said that would not bother him, and they struck a bargain for his services.

Though most folk did not like Glam, all went well until the morning of Yule Eve. Glam rose early and called for food, and Thorhall's wife told him it was not proper to eat on this day since the morrow was the first day of Yule.

"You may fast if you like, but I will not," said Glam. "For I do not hold with your beliefs nor do I go to your church. Now bring me food."

"I think that things will go ill with you because of this," said the mistress. But she was afraid to refuse him and brought him food. He ate and went off to attend the stock.

Shortly after he left the hall, the day became dark, and it began to snow. Thorhall and his folk went to Mass and returned to the stead, but by evening Glam had not returned. The next morning he had still not returned, and after Mass, Thorhall sent men to look for him. They found the sheep and cattle scattered everywhere, but saw no sign of Glam. Finally they came on tracks that led up into the hills, and when they followed them, they came to a hollow where the earth was torn up as if a great struggle had taken place there. And in the center of the hollow was Glam. He was dead; his bones broken and his body black and swollen to enormous size.

Though the men were overcome with horror, they tried to bring his body down, but they could not carry it beyond the edge of the hollow. So they left it and went back to tell Thorhall what they had found. He asked them how they thought Glam had died, and they said they thought that the evil spirit that had been there before had come on Glam and killed him. But they also thought that Glam had given the evil spirit great

wounds, for there were bloody tracks leading up farther into the hills. And, in truth, no more was ever
seen of the evil spirit.

The next day the men went out again with oxen to
bring Glam's body down to the churchyard. But even
the oxen could only drag him a little way, and they
took that to be a sign that he was not to be buried in
the churchyard, so they buried him there in the hills
under a pile of stones.

Soon after that, Glam's ghost began to walk, and
those who met him were either killed or badly injured,
and some who only saw him lost their wits. Many who
lived in those parts were so terrified that they moved
away.

In the spring, when the days lengthened, Glam's
ghost was seen less and less, and folk began to think
that perhaps the evil had passed. But when winter drew
in, he began again to ride the rooftops at night and
became even more violent. He slew two of Thorhall's
men and began raiding farther and farther afield, killing men and cattle all up and down the valley, so that
few dared to abide there. And that was the way it was
now and why much of the vale was deserted.

Grettir was silent when Jokull had finished this tale,
and then he asked where Thorhall was now.

"He is at his stead," said Jokull, "he and his wife
alone, for none now dare stay with him. But I think he
will soon leave there as he did this winter past, because

now that the nights grow long, the ghost becomes more violent than ever."

"I think that I will go and visit Thorhall," said Grettir.

"I would counsel you against it," said Jokull. "Evil cometh from evil. It is hard enough contending with evil men, but a ghost is even worse to deal with."

"I have dealt with ghosts before," said Grettir. "Let us see how I fare with this one."

The next day he rode up the deserted valley to Thorhall's stead. Thorhall was delighted to see him and even more delighted to hear that he wished to spend the night there. "For," he said, "you must have heard what is happening here."

"That is why I came," said Grettir.

They locked Grettir's horse in the stable, and though there was no sign of Glam's ghost about the house that night, when they went to the stable in the morning there was Grettir's horse dead with every bone in its body broken.

Thorhall said that was a bad sign and advised Grettir to leave before nightfall. "If you do not," he said, "I fear it may be your doom."

"My horse was a good one, and I owe it something," said Grettir. "I will not take less for its life than a sight of the evil wight who slew it."

"That is a sight which I do not think you will enjoy," said Thorhall. "For he looks not human."

But Grettir still said he would stay, and when the night came, he stretched out on a bench in the hall in front of Thorhall's enclosed bed and covered himself with a fur cloak. About midnight there was a loud noise as of something trampling on the roof and tearing at it. Then the door opened, and by the dim glow of the night light that burned in the hall, Grettir could make out Glam's shape. He was huge, much larger than a man, standing almost as tall as the roof beams above. His head was big; his hair long and matted, and as he looked about, his eyes glowed like the eyes of a beast.

Glam came into the hall, and seeing the cloak, he took hold of it. But Grettir held on to it, too, bracing his feet against a crossbeam, and Glam could not pull it away from him. Glam tugged even harder, so hard that he lifted Grettir up off the bench, and the cloak was torn in two between the two of them. Then Grettir leaped forward and took Glam around the waist, and a great struggle began. Back and forth they swayed, smashing into benches and tables and shattering them. Glam was trying to drag Grettir out of the hall and into the open, and Grettir was trying to hold back and stay within. But great as Grettir's strength was, Glam slowly pulled him toward the door. When they reached it and Grettir saw that he could no longer hold back, instead of resisting, he drove forward as hard as he could. Glam was not prepared for this, and

he reeled backward, tearing away the door posts and lintel, and falling on his back with Grettir on top of him.

The moon was full and shining brightly, and by its light Grettir saw Glam's face and his great, gray warlock's eyes glaring up at him. And this was so horrible a sight that for the first time in his life Grettir felt dread. And what with this and his great weariness, he had not the strength to draw his sword.

Then Glam spoke and said, "Fiercely have you fought, Grettir, and you have conquered. But I say to you that you will gain little from your victory. For though you are now stronger than all other men, your strength will never grow greater than it is now. More than that, whatever luck you had will now leave you, and all your deeds will turn against you and lead to outlawry, so that you will be forced to live alone, hunted like a wolf. But the worst part of the curse I lay on you is this: that whenever you are in the dark, you will see my eyes, and so you will be afraid to be alone, and this will lead you to your death."

As Glam finished speaking, Grettir's weakness left him, and drawing his sword, he cut off Glam's head and laid it between his thighs as he had done with Kar the Old. Then Thorhall came out of the house and praised God and thanked Grettir for what he had done. Together they piled wood on Glam's body and burned it and then carried the ashes far away and buried them.

It was daylight when they had finished, and Grettir was stiff and sore and weary and lay down to rest. But Thorhall sent for those who still lived in those parts and told them what Grettir had done, and all agreed that this was the greatest deed that any had heard of and one that had brought the most good, since Grettir had not merely helped them but had again made the valley a safe place in which to live when they had given up all hope of that.

The next day Thorhall gave Grettir his best horse to take the place of the one that had been killed and fine clothes, for those he had been wearing were all torn. Thorhall and his neighbors thanked him again for what he had done, and they parted in warm friendship.

Grettir rode home to Bjarg and told all there what had happened, and they, too, said that it was a great deed that he had done. But his brother Atli said, "I do not like what you have told me. For while we are all Christians now, there are old, dark forces here that still have power. And it might well be that with Glam's death your luck has ended."

"I do not believe in luck," said Grettir. "A man makes his own fate."

"You say that because you have been fortunate so far, and though you are still young, you are already one of the most famous men in Iceland. But no wind blows always from the same quarter."

"Are you telling me that things will now go ill with me?" said Grettir.

"I am telling you to be careful and watch your temper. For if you do not—and there is anything in what Glam said—it could lead to serious trouble."

Grettir said he would be as careful as he could be, but he was afraid that now his temper would be shorter than ever. For Glam's curse was already beginning to work, and now when he was alone at night, he saw Glam's eyes and other terrible things, and so he had become fearful of the dark and slept very badly.

Grettir spent the winter at Bjarg, and Atli saw that what he had said was true. For often during the night Grettir would cry out and wake up and seize his weapons. When this happened, Atli would talk to him and quiet him. But he could see how it would be a hard thing for Grettir if he were alone and there were no one by him to whom he could speak when he woke this way, thinking he must again fight Glam's ghost.

9

The Slaying of Thorbjorn the Slow and Grettir's Second Voyage to Norway

D URING that winter there was much talk about how Grettir had helped the people of Vatnsdal by ridding the valley of Glam's ghost. But when word of it came to Thorbjorn the Slow, he was jealous of this new deed of Grettir's and made little of it. Instead he talked about what had happened after the horse fight when he and his kinsman, Oxmain, had come between Grettir's party and Kormak's, and made them stop their battle. Grettir had not seemed very brave or eager to fight then, he claimed. Many who heard this thought that Grettir would have something to say about it if he and Thorbjorn met, and they were not wrong.

In the spring there came a ship from Norway bringing the news that Olaf, the son of Harald, was now king, having driven the Earl Sveinn from the country. Since the earl with whom Grettir had had so much trouble over the slaying of the three brothers was now gone, Grettir thought he would go to Norway again and take service with the king. For it was said that Olaf was showing his favor to all brave men and making them his followers.

Asmund, Grettir's father, was by this time quite old and so ill that he did not often leave his bed. But besides Atli, who was managing the estate, Asmund now had a fourth son named Illugi, so Grettir did not think he would be missed. Saying good-bye to his father and all the others at Bjarg, he rode to the coast where he had arranged to take a ship to Norway.

Now Thorbjorn had taken passage on that same vessel, not knowing that Grettir would be aboard. When Thorbjorn's friends heard that the two men would be sailing together, they tried to persuade Thorbjorn to wait for another ship, but he said he would not delay his sailing for Grettir or anyone else.

True to his name, Thorbjorn arrived at the port late, long after Grettir had gotten there. As he dismounted, men asked him if he brought word of any new happenings.

"None of any great importance," he said. "Only that Asmund of Bjarg is dead."

Many said that that was too bad, for he was a good and brave man.

"Well, he did not die bravely," said Thorbjorn, "for he was smothered like a dog by the smoke of his hearth fire. But that was no great loss, for he had already become a dotard."

Now Grettir came forward and said, "What you have just said is not only a lie—for Asmund is not dead —but a shameful lie."

"Nevertheless I will not unsay it," said Thorbjorn.

"Then I prophesy that you will not die either of old age or of smoke from the hearth," said Grettir. "Defend yourself, for you will never have greater need to do so."

Thorbjorn drew his sword, and Grettir struck at him, and it was such a great blow that it beat down Thorbjorn's guard and cut through his neck and that was his death.

The watching sailors said that it was a mighty stroke and that he who dealt it was just the man for King Olaf. No one should mourn for Thorbjorn, they said, for he was a quarrelsome and spiteful man with a tongue that was as long and poisonous as an adder's. Then they all went aboard the ship and set sail for Norway.

10

The Fetching of the Fire
and What Came of It

S UMMER was over when Grettir arrived in Norway, landing in the south. There he learned that King Olaf was at Thrandheim in the north, and he took passage with some traders who were sailing that way up the coast.

The bad weather began early that year, and their passage was slow. Winter had already set in when the ship on which Grettir was sailing neared Stad. The weather worsened, and it began to snow, and finally all those on board became so worn-out and cold that they put in and took shelter under a bank. They all went ashore, but they were little better off now than they had been, for they had no fire and they feared that they would not live through the night.

Then, as the darkness settled on them, they saw a fire on the far side of the sound. At first they thought to sail over to it, but they finally agreed that it would be too dangerous as the storm still raged. They began to talk about whether there was any man who was brave and hardy enough to cross the sound and bring back fire.

Grettir had paid little attention to their talk, but now he said it did not seem such a great feat to him.

"Then will you do it, Grettir?" they asked. "For our need is great, and it will not only help us, but it will prove that the people of Iceland speak the truth when they talk of your prowess."

"I fear what will come of it if I should go," he said.

"How could anything but good come of it?" they asked. "Do you think we will not honor and reward you if you should do it?"

"I tell you I fear what will come of it," said Grettir. "Nevertheless, if your need is so great, I will go."

He stripped to his breeches and tied his cloak around his waist. Then, taking a small cask in which to carry the fire, he dived into the icy waters of the sound, and swimming strongly against the wind and tide, he reached the other side. There he saw a rough shelter and went toward it.

Now in the shelter there were some dozen men, and among them there were two Icelanders, the sons of Thorir of Gard, an important chieftain. Like Grettir, the sons of Thorir had come to Norway to take service with King Olaf. And like him they had been sailing north to Thrandheim and had put in to shore to wait for better weather. They had found a hut, built as a shelter for those who traveled those parts, and had been there for several days now. They were sitting around a great fire and drinking when the door burst open and Grettir came in. His cloak had frozen and stood out stiffly around him, and his hair was wild and white with ice and snow. What with their drinking and their surprise, those in the hut thought he was some troll or evil spirit come in from the storm and began to call out and attack him. They struck at him with anything that

came to hand, even burning brands from the fire, and some of the brands fell on the straw that covered the floor and set it alight.

Grettir fended off his attackers as best he could, caught up embers in his cask, and went out again. He swam back across the sound, and his companions praised him mightily for his deed and, building a fire of their own, spent the night in warmth and comfort.

The next day the weather turned fair, and the traders with whom Grettir was sailing took their ship across the sound to see who it was from whom Grettir had fetched the fire. But when they came ashore, they found no shelter but only a heap of ashes and among them the burned bones of men.

Now the traders turned on Grettir and said that he must have done this and that it was a terrible and wicked deed. Grettir said that he had not done it, but that if it had happened because of his coming to get the fire, it was no less than what he had expected.

Then the traders sailed off, refusing to carry Grettir with them. But that was not the worst of the hurt they caused him. For wherever they went, they told the tale of the burning, so that no other trader would carry Grettir on his ship and no man would have anything to do with him.

With great difficulty Grettir made his way north, for he was determined to appear before the king and tell him the truth of what had happened. When he arrived at Thrandheim, he went before the king and told him the true tale of the fetching of the fire, and the king said, "It may well be that what you say is the truth, and you did not do this deed."

"I swear that I did not," said Grettir. "Those in the hut were all alive when I left with the fire. And I will undergo any ordeal you decree to prove that I am innocent."

"So be it," said King Olaf. "Then you shall bear iron, and that shall be the proof of what you say."

Grettir said he was content at this and immediately began fasting for the trial: an ordeal in which he would carry red-hot iron in his hand and, after three days, show that he had taken no hurt from it.

On the day set for the ordeal, Grettir went to the church. The king and the bishop were there and many folk, for all had heard of Grettir and wanted to see him. But as Grettir started down the aisle, a great, over-grown, and ugly boy jumped up and cried, "Here is a fine thing, a murderer coming into church to prove that he is innocent! For we all know that he is guilty no matter what happens in the ordeal!"

Then he began making faces at Grettir and pointing at him and calling him names, and this so enraged Grettir that he gave him a great box on the ear, and the boy fell down senseless. Then there was great confusion in the church, and the king came forward and said, "You are a man doomed to misfortune, Grettir.

All was ready for the ordeal, but now that you have so disturbed the peace, it cannot take place."

"I hoped for better than that from you, O king," said Grettir. "I came here to Thrandheim to take service with you."

"And I would have welcomed you," said the king. "For there are few who are your equal in strength or bravery. But your luck is too bad for me to keep you with me. I give you leave to remain here in Norway for the winter, but next summer you must return to Iceland."

"But what of the charge of burning?" asked Grettir. "For that is something of which I am innocent and would clear myself."

"It is likely that the tale you tell is true," said the king. "Yet since the trial by ordeal has come to naught because of your short temper, we cannot put it to the test. So you must bear what will be said about you as best you can."

Then the king left the church. But when the people began to look for the boy who had so provoked Grettir, they could not find him nor did any know who he was. And so, many believed that he was some imp or evil wight come there to do hurt to Grettir. In this way did the curse that Glam had laid upon him begin to work. For now, like King Olaf, even those who did not turn against him considered him a man doomed to misfortune. And this is a hard thing for any man to bear.

11

The Slaying of Snaekoll and Second Meeting with Thorsteinn

GRETTIR remained for a while longer at Thrand-heim, but when he found that further speech with the king gained him nothing, he started south to see his brother Thorsteinn again. For he had not forgotten how Thorsteinn had come to his aid and stood by him when the Earl Sveinn would have had his life during his last voyage to Norway.

At Yuletide, Grettir arrived at the stead of a land-owner named Einar. Einar was a wealthy man with a comely daughter who was of an age to be married. Einar invited Grettir to spend Yule with him, and Grettir accepted.

Now despite what the Earl Sveinn had tried to do about it, it was still not uncommon for outlaws and ruffians to come in from the outlands and make trouble for honest men. They would challenge the landowners to fight for their women and their wealth, and if they refused or there were not enough men at the stead to protect it, they would carry off what they wanted. One of the worst of these outlaws was a huge berserk named Snaekoll.

During the Yule season, Snaekoll and a large party of like villains rode up to Einar's house. Snaekoll told Einar that if he were man enough, he must fight him. If not, he must hand over his daughter to him.

Now Einar was no longer a young man, and he had never been a great fighter, so he asked Grettir what he should do.

"You must not do aught that will bring shame upon you," said Grettir. "I will go out with you, and we will talk to this fellow together."

They went out of the house to where Snaekoll was sitting on his horse with his men behind him. He was wearing his helmet and carrying his iron-rimmed shield, and mighty fierce he looked.

"Well, what have you decided?" asked Snaekoll. "Shall I have the girl, or will you fight? Or if you your-self will not fight, perhaps that lumpish churl with you would like to trade handstrokes with me."

"There is little to choose between us there," said

Grettir. "For neither of us is greatly skilled in such play."

"Then it is no wonder that you are afraid to fight me," said Snaekoll. "And you will be even more afraid if you keep me waiting and I grow angry."

"That is a sight that I would like to see," said Grettir. "For you are ugly enough as it is."

"Do you mock me?" cried Snaekoll. And with that the berserk fury came on him, and he bit the edge of his shield and howled into it, so that the sound echoed throughout the stead. As he did, Grettir stepped forward and kicked the bottom of the shield such a great kick that the upper edge drove up and broke Snaekoll's jaw. Then, seizing the chin strap of the berserk's helmet, he pulled him from his horse. At the same time Grettir drew his sword, and even while Snaekoll was falling, he cut off his head with a single stroke.

A moment Snaekoll's followers sat there amazed; then all fled as if the devil himself were after them.

Einar thanked Grettir much for this deed, and so did all the others in those parts. For he had not only rid them of a fearsome scourge, but all considered that he had done so with great courage and skill.

Grettir stayed with Einar through the Yule season, then he went on to Tunsberg where his brother Thorsteinn welcomed him joyfully. Thorsteinn had heard about the burning of Thorir's sons, and first they talked about that, and then Thorsteinn asked him about the

slaying of the berserk. Grettir gave him an account of
that and finished with a verse:

> *Fierce was Snaekoll and bright his shield*
> *When Einar he pressed his daughter to yield.*
> *Yet the shield that should his life have saved*
> *Was the weapon with which I slew the knave.*

They were sitting by the fire at the time, and since
it was very warm, they had stripped off their upper

garments. Thorsteinn looked at Grettir's arms, which were bare, and said, "I do not wonder that you can strike such blows, brother. For never have I seen mightier arms than yours."

"They have served me well enough," said Grettir.

"And still," said Thorsteinn, "it seems to me that you might have a happier life if your arms were not so strong and your luck was better."

"No man makes either himself or his fortune," said Grettir. "Let me see your arms."

He looked at them. And while Thorsteinn was a tall man and well knit, he was lean, and his arms were nowise so mighty as Grettir's.

"Well," said Grettir, "I suppose that they will do."

"It is true that they are not much compared to yours," said Thorsteinn. "Yet it may well be that one day they shall avenge you."

"If that should come to pass, I shall not know it," said Grettir. "So, on the chance that it may, let me thank you for it now."

No more is told of what they said to one another. They spent the winter and spring together in warm friendship and brotherhood, and in the summer Grettir took ship for Iceland.

12

The Death of Asmund and
the Slaying of Atli

D URING the time that Grettir was away in Norway, there were many happenings in Iceland. His
father, Asmund, who had been sick when Grettir left,
grew no better. When he felt his end was near, he
called in his kinsmen and told them that his son Atli
should have his property when he was gone.

"And I ask you to support him," he said. "For I fear
that there are those who will not leave him in peace.
Grettir, too, will need your help for, strong though he
is, he is a man born to trouble. As for Illugi, the third of
my sons by my wife Asdis, I can say little about him,
for he is still young. But I think that if no harm comes
to him till he is grown, he will be a man of brave deeds."

Shortly after that, Asmund died and was buried

in the yard of the church he had built at Bjarg, and all
mourned his passing.

Toward the end of summer, Atli rode west to
the coast to buy dried fish. His kinsman Grim rode
with him, and they had four men with them. Now
Thorbjorn Oxmain was still angry at all those in Bjarg,
because Grettir had killed his kinsman Thorbjorn the
Slow. When he heard that Atli had journeyed west,
he knew that he must return past his stead, and he
set two of his followers to waylay him. They were

Gunnar and Thorgeir, and they were no strangers to those of Bjarg, for they had been with Oxmain when he had come upon Grettir's men and Kormak's when they were battling on the heath after the horse fight and had made them cease. In fact it had been Gunnar who had killed one of Atli's men.

This was in Atli's mind when Gunnar, Thorgeir, and their party came upon him and Grim and their men, and Atli asked them if they had come to offer blood money for his servant.

"If we are to talk of blood money," said Gunnar, "I would rather talk of that which is owed for Thorbjorn the Slow whom Grettir slew. For he was worth many times your man."

"There is little to be gained in talking about that," said Atli, "for you are no kin of Thorbjorn's and cannot represent him."

"But you are kin of Grettir's and can pay with your life for the life he took," said Gunnar. And with that he and his party set on Atli and his men.

The fighting was long and fierce, and at first it looked ill for those from Bjarg for they were only six to Gunnar and Thorgeir's eight. But in the end Atli killed Gunnar, and Grim killed Thorgeir, and that settled the matter. Atli gave quarter to those of the attackers who were left and rode on home.

Thorbjorn Oxmain was angrier than ever at the slaying of Gunnar and Thorgeir and brought suit against Atli and Grim at the local Thing early the next summer.

Both sides were well represented, but Atli was liked by all and considered a peaceful man, and finally a settlement was worked out. Atli was to pay a fine for the killings, but only half the usual amount, for he had been attacked, and Grim was to be banished, not from Iceland, but just from the district.

Atli was satisfied with the judgement, but Thorbjorn was not. Though he accepted it, he said that more might still come of the matter.

Now Thorbjorn had a servant named Ali, who was both lazy and impudent. One day, shortly after the meeting of the Thing, they had a quarrel, and Thorbjorn gave Ali a sound beating. Ali ran away and, crossing the neck of the fjord, went to Bjarg where he asked Atli for work.

"Are you not one of Thorbjorn's men?" asked Atli.

"I was, but we did not get on," said Ali. "I would like to work for you if you will have me."

"I have men enough of my own without taking them from Thorbjorn," said Atli. "And I have also had more than enough trouble with him. You had better go back to him."

"That I will never do no matter what happens," said Ali.

He stayed overnight at Bjarg, and the next morning he went out with Atli's men and worked as if he were

not one man but several. Atli said nothing more to him, but since he liked the way he worked, he let him stay on at Bjarg for the time being, giving him food and shelter.

A few days later Thorbjorn heard that Ali was at Bjarg and rode over there with two men.

"It seems you are determined to make me angry, Atli," said Thorbjorn. "Why have you taken one of my men away from me?"

"I did not take him," said Atli. "He came here of his own free will. And he claims that he is not your man and that he left because you did not get on."

"I say he is my man," said Thorbjorn.

"If he is and he wants to go with you, he can go," said Atli. "But if he wants to stay here, I will not drive him away."

"If he does not return to me and I have to come here again, you will be sorry, Atli," said Thorbjorn, and he and his men rode back to his stead.

When the men came in from the fields that evening, Atli told Ali that Thorbjorn had been there and again said Ali should go back to him, for he did not want another quarrel with him.

"It seems that there is truth in the old saying 'Often those who are praised are overpraised,' " said Ali. "I had always heard that you were a just man. But now after I have worked so hard for you, you are going to send me back to a place where I will be beaten."

At this, Atli changed his mind and said he could stay. Time passed, but Thorbjorn's anger at Atli did not lessen. One day, just before midsummer when haying was beginning, Thorbjorn armed himself, putting on a helmet and taking a broad-bladed spear in his hand, and rode again to Bjarg.

It was a rainy day, and most of the men were away, but Atli was at home. Thorbjorn knocked on the door, then went around to the side of the house, and hid. One of the women came out and, seeing no one there, went back in again. Atli asked her who had knocked, and she said she did not know, that whoever it was must have gone. At that moment Thorbjorn knocked again, even more loudly.

"No, he is still here," said Atli. "And it sounds as if his business is urgent."

He went to the door himself and opened it, peering out into the rain. Seeing the man he was looking for, Thorbjorn came around the side of the house and drove at Atli with his spear, piercing him through the middle.

"Spears come with broad blades these days," said Atli. Then he fell dead.

By the time Atli's mother, Asdis, and the other women of the house came out, Thorbjorn had mounted his horse. He announced that he had done the killing and rode home.

Atli was buried next to his father, and there was

great grief at his death, for he was a wise and good man
and much loved. No blood money was paid for his
death because the proper person to bring suit for it was
Grettir, his nearest kinsman, and he was not in Iceland.
Thorbjorn stayed quietly at home after the killing, but
he got little praise for this deed.

13

The Outlawing of Grettir and His Return to Iceland

THAT same summer, before the meeting of the All-Thing, word came from Norway about what had happened early the past winter when Grettir had fetched the fire near Stad. Thorir of Gard, whose sons had died when the shelter burned down, was beside himself with rage when he heard the news and vowed vengeance on Grettir.

He rode to the Thing with a large following and presented the case against Grettir, demanding that he be outlawed. Then spoke Skapti, who had been appointed Lawman by the All-Thing because it was thought that he had the greatest knowledge of the law of any in the land.

"If the burning took place as we have heard, that was certainly an evil deed and a great crime," said Skapti.

"But as has been said, 'The tale of one man is but half a tale.' Therefore I hold that no judgement should be taken against Grettir until he has had a chance to tell his side of the story."

Now Skapti was considered a wise and just man, and his word carried the greatest of weight. Therefore there were many at the Thing who thought that it should be as he said and that the case should not be decided until Grettir's return. But there were others who said that Skapti was kin of Grettir's, and since Thorir was an important chieftain with many powerful friends and pressed the matter hard, in the end the case was decided against Grettir, and he was declared an outlaw and a price put upon his head.

Later in the summer Grettir returned, landing in the west in the Borgarfjord. When he came ashore, people there told him all that had happened and he spoke a verse:

> *Black the news and heavy and hard*
> *That awaited the wandering, returning bard:*
> *Father and brother both are dead*
> *And a price in silver set on my head.*
> *Yet I say to you that more than one*
> *Shall rue their deeds ere the tale be done.*

He took horse and rode east to where his kinsman Grim had been living since he was banished from his

home district. Grim told Grettir that all he had heard was true. That no boot had been paid for the killing of Atli, and that Thorbjorn Oxmain had become so high-handed that there was some question as to whether Grettir's mother, Asdis, would be able to continue living at Bjarg.

"We shall see about that," said Grettir.

Grettir stayed only a short time with Grim, for he did not want it known that he was about to travel north across the heath. Though Grim knew that he himself would be outlawed if it was learned that he had harbored an outlaw, he told Grettir to come back and stay with him again if he had need of a safe place. But Grettir said his need would have to be very great before he did that. Then he took horse again and rode north across the heath to Bjarg.

When he arrived there it was late, past midnight, and all were asleep save his mother. He went into the hall by a back door and was groping his way towards his mother's close-bed when she said, "Is that my son, Grettir?"

"Yes, Mother," he answered.

"I thought it was," she said. "Come here."

He went to the bed, and she sat up and kissed him and said, "Welcome home, son. And welcome all the more since I now have one son less than when you went away."

"I know, Mother," he said. "And I also know about my father. You have drunk from a bitter cup since I sailed for Norway."

"Yes, it was bitter," she said. "And it has not been sweetened by your having been declared an outlaw."

"That I can endure," he said. "About my father's death I can do nothing. But the slaying of Atli is another matter. That will not go long unavenged."

"No," she said. "That was in my mind, too, when I heard your step in the hall and knew that you were home again: that there was one whose span of days could now be numbered."

14

The Slaying of Thorbjorn Oxmain

G RETTIR stayed quietly at Bjarg, and the folk there said naught about it, for he did not want it known that he was back in the district. At the same time, he had word brought to him of the comings and goings of Thorbjorn Oxmain.

One day he heard that Thorbjorn was at home and that he had only a few men with him, for this was the haying season. And so Grettir took his horse and rode west across the ridge to his stead. He arrived there about noon and knocked on the door and asked for Thorbjorn. The women there did not know Grettir and said that Thorbjorn was in the fields with his son, Arnor. Grettir thanked them and rode down to the fields.

Thorbjorn and Arnor had bound up one load of hay

and were beginning a second when Grettir reached the field where they were working. He was too far away for them to recognize him; nevertheless they stopped their work and took up their weapons.

Grettir got off his horse. He wore a helmet, and besides his sword he carried a great spear. He knocked out the rivet that held the spear head to the shaft so that Thorbjorn would not be able to cast the spear back at him. Then he went on again.

"That is a big man," said Thorbjorn to Arnor. "He is so big that he must be Grettir Asmundson. It is not hard to guess why he has come, but I have not yet met a single man against whom I could not stand. Still it would be well to be careful. So while I engage him, do you go around behind him and strike at him with your ax."

Grettir had now come within casting distance, and he sped his spear at Thorbjorn. But the head was looser than he thought, and it fell from the shaft and did Thorbjorn no hurt. Thorbjorn drew his sword and raised his shield and advanced on Grettir. Grettir drew his sword also, but seeing that Arnor was coming around behind him, he stood not still but kept always moving. Thorbjorn and Arnor came at Grettir, both together. But Arnor was the closer, and when Grettir saw that he was within reach, he struck back over his shoulder and shattered Arnor's skull, and that was his death.

Then Thorbjorn rushed upon Grettir and struck at
him. Grettir caught the stroke on his shield and fended
it off. Then he in turn struck at Thorbjorn, and it was
such a mighty blow that it cut Thorbjorn's shield in
two and went into his brain, and there was no need

for Grettir to strike again, for that one stroke was Thorbjorn's death also.

Grettir mounted his horse and rode to the nearest settlement where he proclaimed the slayings; then he rode home to Bjarg.

His mother met him at the door and asked, "Is it done?"

"It is done, Mother," said Grettir.

"Now do I know that you are truly of the Vatnsdal blood," she said. "But now also will the hard lot of your outlawry begin. For this is the first place to which Thorbjorn's kinsmen will come when they begin looking for you, so you cannot stay here. What will you do?"

Grettir said he would go to the west and stay with his friends and kinsmen there. He got together what he needed for traveling and said good-bye to his mother with much love, telling his youngest brother, Illugi, to watch out for her; then he left Bjarg.

He went first to see his brother-in-law, Gamli, and gave him an account of all that had happened. Gamli told him it would be better if he did not stay in those parts while Thorbjorn's kinsmen were looking for him, but said he would support him as best he could in the suit over the slayings. Grettir thanked him and rode west over the heath to the coast, where he stayed with his kinsman Thorsteinn Kuggason until well into autumn.

15

The Attempt to Avenge Thorbjorn
and the Suit at the Thing

THORODD Drapustuf was Thorbjorn's brother, so it
fell on him to take up the blood feud and avenge
the slayings of Thorbjorn and his son, Arnor. He
called out his men and rode to the settlement nearby,
and when he heard that Grettir had proclaimed to all
here that he had done the killings, he went on to Bjarg
and asked for him there.

"He is not here," said Asdis. "If he were, he would
not hide from you. But since in slaying Thorbjorn he
was only avenging the killing of his brother Atli, I
would advise you to let the matter end there."

Thorodd said he could not do that. He saw, however, that there was no more to be done at Bjarg, so he
rode home. Several times during the fall and winter

Thorodd had word of Grettir. But always when he
went with men to look for him, Grettir had been
warned and was gone.

When the time came for the meeting of the All-
Thing, Thorodd rode there with a large following and
laid his complaint against Grettir for the slayings.
Grettir's friends and kinsmen consulted with Skapti
the Lawman, and he said their case seemed to be a good
one and he would do what he could to help them.

The case went before the judges, and it was their opinion that the slaying of Thorbjorn and Atli should be set off, one against the other. Now Skapti thought he had come upon a way in which he could truly help Grettir, so he went before the judges and asked them how they had arrived at their decision. They said they had done so because Atli and Thorbjorn were both of equal rank.

"That is true," said Skapti. "But which happened first, the outlawing of Grettir or the slaying of Atli?"

They reckoned up the matter and found that while Grettir had been outlawed at the last Thing, Atli had been slain a week or so afterward.

"That is what I thought," said Skapti. "You have made a mistake. You have treated Grettir as a party in the case when he was an outlaw who could not appear as either plaintiff or defendant. Now I say that he has nothing to do with the case and that action against Thorbjorn must be brought by Atli's nearest kin who are still within the law."

"But then who is to answer for the slaying of my brother, Thorbjorn?" asked Thorodd.

"I do not know," said Skapti. "But I say this to you —Grettir's kinsmen will surely not pay for his deeds while he is still an outlaw."

Now Grettir's kinsmen saw what Skapti had in his mind. Those nearest of kin to Atli after Grettir came forward and took up the case against Thorbjorn for slaying Atli. And since Grettir could not be a party to the suit and his slaying of Thorbjorn could not be set off against Thorbjorn's slaying of Atli, Thorodd was told he must pay a fine of five marks of silver for Atli's death.

Then spoke the chief of the judges, saying, "It seems to me, Thorodd, that things have come out differently than you expected. For here, because Grettir is an outlaw, you will have to pay a fine for Atli's death and get nothing for the death of Thorbjorn. Now are you willing that the sentence of outlawry against Grettir should be lifted? If you are, then the two killings can be set off against one another, and you will have to pay nothing. Not only that, but I suspect that if Grettir remains an outlaw, many will suffer because of it."

Grettir's kinsmen were well pleased at this proposal and said they would be glad to forget about the money if the sentence against Grettir was lifted. Thorodd said that now that he had seen how complicated the case had become, he would accept the proposal, too.

But the chief of the judges said that they must ask Thorir of Gard whether he also would accept the proposal, for it was he who had brought the suit against Grettir for the burning of his two sons. Then came Thorir before them and said angrily that he would never consent to having the sentence against Grettir removed. That not only would he not consent to it, but he would raise the price that had been put on Grettir's head, so that it would be higher than any ever put on the head of any outlaw.

And so the attempt to free Grettir of his sentence came to naught. Thorodd had to pay the fine for Atli's killing and got no compensation for the deaths of Thorbjorn and Arnor. Thorodd and Thorir each offered a reward of three marks of silver for Grettir's head, and most folk agreed with the chief of the judges that it was not a wise thing to go to such lengths to keep Grettir an outlaw when he could be given peace and freedom, for he was a man who could make much trouble.

16

The Meeting with Lopt

AFTER the All-Thing, Grettir began more and more to feel the weight of his outlawry, for because of the high price that had been put upon his head, many of those who had always been friendly to him were less willing to take him in. Or if they did take him in, they were not anxious to have him stay too long.

Late in the fall Grettir went south and west again and spent the winter with his kinsman Thorsteinn Kuggason. But in the spring Thorodd heard where he was and gathered men to take him, so Grettir moved farther south and stayed with other kinsmen and friends until that summer's assembly at the Thing was over.

After the Thing, Grettir went north and began living on Kjol, a mountain near the center of Iceland, overlooking an important road. Since he was alone, he was much troubled by Glam's curse, seeing that evil wight's ghostly eyes and other frightening things in the dark. And since he was living out in the open, he had now to stop those who went by and take from them whatever he needed in the way of food, clothing, and weapons, and there were none who dared say him nay.

One day he saw a man come riding down the valley road. He was a big man; his horse was a fine one, and he led another horse that was loaded with goods. Grettir went up to him, and as the man wore a wide-brimmed hat that shadowed his face, he asked his name.

"You may call me Lopt," said the man.

Since *lopt* means air, Grettir said, "That is a strange name for a man to have."

"Then perhaps it is not my name," said Lopt. "But I know who you are. You are Grettir whom they call the Strong. Whither are you going?"

"I never know from day to day," said Grettir. "But what I would ask you is whether you will share your goods with me."

"Why should I do that?" asked Lopt.

"If you have heard of me, then you must know that most men are glad to give me what I want and not ask for payment."

"But I am not like most men," said Lopt. "I do not give up my goods for nothing." And he started to ride on.

"Not so fast," said Grettir, and he seized the horse's bridle and checked it.

"Do not try and keep me here, Grettir," said Lopt. "You will get nothing from me as long as I am able to hold it."

"Well, let us see if you can," said Grettir.

"As you wish," said Lopt. Reaching down, he took hold of the bridle. And though Grettir gripped it as tightly as he could, he wrenched it away from him. Grettir looked down at his hands, then up again. And now he knew that he had to do, not with a mortal man, but with one of the land-spirits.

"What is your true name?" asked Grettir.

"Hallmund," said the tall rider. "And I dwell under Balljokull beyond the Arnavatn Heath. I tell you this because it is in my mind that we shall meet again—and you will not regret that meeting—and then you will come and visit me there."

He smiled and nodded to Grettir, and again urged his horse forward, and this time Grettir did not try to stop him, and he rode off.

After this meeting, Grettir rode south and asked Skapti the Lawman if he might stay with him.

"Word has come to me that you have become a robber," said Skapti. "Is this true?"

"It is true that I have taken that which I needed in order to live without paying for it," said Grettir.

"You know that I am your friend and that I tried to

have the sentence that was passed on you lifted," said Skapti. "It is not only unbecoming for someone of your birth to rob men of their goods, but it makes it more difficult for me to do anything for you. As for staying with me, since I am the Lawman, how do you think it would look for me to break the law myself by giving shelter to an outlaw?"

"It would not look well," said Grettir. "But then where am I to go and what am I to do?"

"You must go to some place where you can live without robbery," said Skapti.

"That I would be glad to do," said Grettir. "But you must know that there is another burden that I carry. And that is that because of the curse which Glam put upon me, I fear the dark, and it is a hard and grievous thing for me to live alone."

"No one has said that the life of an outlaw was an easy one," said Skapti. "But you must put up with it as best you can. My advice to you is to go back north to some lonely place like the Arnavatn Heath and live there. But be careful if any come to you and offer to live with you, for there are many who wish your death."

Grettir thanked Skapti for his good advice and said he would follow it.

17

Treachery on the Heath

GRETTIR went up to the Arnavatn Heath and built himself a hut near a lake. And because Skapti had urged him to give over robbing other men, he got himself a boat and nets, and lived on the fish he caught in the lake. This was a bad time for him because it was a lonely place at best, but his fear of the dark made it even worse for him than it would have been for other men.

One day Thorodd, Thorbjorn Oxmain's brother, heard where Grettir was, and he called to him an outlaw named Grim. This was not of course Gamli's brother, who had ever been Grettir's friend, but an outlaw from the north. Thorodd promised this Grim money and a pardon for his crimes if he would kill

Grettir. Grim went to Grettir's hut on the heath and asked if he could stay with him.

Remembering Skapti's warning, Grettir said, "If you were one who could be trusted, you would not be a forest man, forced to live here in the outlands. Still it is a hard thing to live alone and harder for me than for others. I will take you in, but you must share the work with me."

Grim said he would do whatever was needful, so Grettir took him in. Grim stayed on into the winter with Grettir and watched him closely. It soon became clear to him that it would be no easy thing to attack Grettir, for Grettir was watchful and kept his weapons at hand day and night.

Early one morning Grim came into the hut from fishing and found Grettir still lying by the fire. Grim stamped noisily about to see whether Grettir was truly asleep, but Grettir moved not. Grettir's sword hung over his head, and it seemed to Grim that he would never have a better chance than this, so he drew the sword, raising it to strike. As he did so, Grettir leaped up, seizing the sword with one hand and Grim with the other, and threw him to the ground.

"So this is how you repay me for my hospitality," said Grettir. "Now tell me who sent you here."

Grim told him that he had been sent there by Thorodd, and Grettir slew him. It was then midwinter when the nights were longest and darkest, and because he had had company for some time, from then on Grettir's night fears were harder for him to bear than ever. He would lie awake for long hours, keeping a fire burning and seeming to see, not merely Glam's eyes, but many pairs of eyes gathered in a ring around the hut. And when he fell asleep, he would see those same eyes in his dreams. They would draw in closer and closer to him until he would awake with a loud cry and seize his sword, staring about him wildly. And often he would remain this way, huddled by the fire with his sword in his hand until dawn.

Now Grettir's other great enemy, Thorir of Gard, heard where he was to be found and tried to undo him also. Like Thorodd, he summoned to him an outlaw, this one called Redbeard. Redbeard was one of the strongest men and one of the greatest fighters in Iceland. But when he heard what Thorir wanted him to do, he said, "That will be no easy task. For Grettir was always a watchful man, and now he will be more wary than ever."

"So much the more praise will you get if you can overcome him," said Thorir. Then he told Redbeard what a high price had been set on Grettir's head and said if he could slay him, he would have the sentence of outlawry on Redbeard removed. And in the end Redbeard said he would try it.

Then Redbeard went away into the east and came to the heath from that quarter so that Grettir would

not know where he had been, and asked him for shelter.

"That I cannot give you," said Grettir. "There was one who came here last fall, pretending to be a friend, and before long I found that he had come here to kill me."

"I do not blame you for being careful," said Redbeard. "But while you may have heard that I was a manslayer, it has never been said of me that I betrayed my host, for that is the most monstrous of all crimes. I would not have come here if I had anywhere else to go, for this is the loneliest of places. But lonely as it is and hard our lot, we should be able to endure it if we stand together. Will you not at least let me stay here for a while and see how we get on?"

"I will risk that much," said Grettir. "But know that if I see any sign of treachery, that will be your death."

So Grettir took him in and found Redbeard to be, not only the strongest of men, but the most willing. Whatever it was that needed to be done, Redbeard did it, and life was easier for Grettir than it had been since he first became an outlaw. But with all that, Grettir remained so careful that Redbeard had no chance to come at him.

In this way a full year went by, and then another, and Redbeard became weary of life on the heath and began thinking harder than ever about how he might catch Grettir off guard.

One night in the spring a sudden storm blew up, and

Grettir woke and asked Redbeard if their boat was safe. Redbeard said he would see, and he went down to the lake and stove in the boat so that it would look as if the storm had done it and threw the nets far out into the water.

Then he came back to the hut and said, "We have had bad luck, Grettir. The boat is smashed, and the nets are far out in the lake."

"Then go and get them," said Grettir. "For if anything has happened to the boat, it is your fault."

"You know that since I have been here I have done whatever needed to be done," said Redbeard. "But this I cannot do as the boat cannot be used and you also know that I cannot swim."

Then Grettir got up and took his weapons and went down to the lake and saw that what Redbeard had said was true. A point ran out into the lake in this part, and the water was very deep on both sides of it. Grettir stood on the point and looked out to the middle of the lake where the nets floated, and Redbeard said, "Is it such a difficult task to swim out there and get them?"

"It is not difficult," said Grettir. "But I am still not sure that I can trust you."

"If you do not after all this time," said Redbeard, "then perhaps I should leave the heath."

"Let us make a test of it then," said Grettir, and he stripped off his clothes and put down his weapons and went into the lake. He swam out to where the nets were and gathered them together and swam back to one side of the point. He cast the nets up on the shore and was climbing the bank when Redbeard drew Grettir's sword and ran toward him to cut him down. Grettir threw himself backward, sinking like a stone. Then as Redbeard stood there waiting for him to rise again, Grettir swam underwater around the point and came up on the other side of it. Since it was still night and the only light was that of the fitful moon, Redbeard could not see what he was doing. Grettir came ashore quietly, and the first Redbeard knew of it was when Grettir was behind him. Grettir lifted him up and threw him down again with such force that the sword fell from his hand. Grettir seized it, and without another word he slew Redbeard.

After that, though it was still very hard for him to be alone, Grettir would have naught to do with any other outlaw.

18

The Second Meeting with Hallmund

WHEN Thorir of Gard went to the All-Thing that summer, he learned that Redbeard had been slain and that he must find some other way to take revenge on Grettir for the burning of his sons. He had about eighty men with him, and when he left the Thing, he kept to the west and came on the heath by a roundabout way, hoping to deal with Grettir himself. But Grettir's kinsmen heard of his plans and sent word to Grettir to keep a careful watch.

One day Grettir saw horsemen coming toward his hut, so he left it and went to a place nearby where there was a narrow rift between two great rocks. Then he saw more men and still more, and he knew his plight was serious. For while he could defend himself from the front, it would be no great task for some of Thorir's men to ride around and come at him from the far side of the rift. But it was too late now for him to find another place for a stand, so he prepared to sell his life as dearly as possible.

Now Thorir and his men came up, and Thorir sent some of them around to the other side of the rocks to come on Grettir from the rear as Grettir had feared he would.

"We have him cornered now," said Thorir. "So press on and let us make an end of him."

"Because the cup is filled, that does not mean it will be drunk," said Grettir. "You have come a long way to find me, but there are some of you who will not go home again."

Then Thorir's men began their attack, and Grettir fought them off, always waiting for those who would come at him from the back. But they came not. Finally when many of Thorir's men had been killed and others wounded, Thorir said, "I have always heard that Grettir was a man of strength and courage and greatly skilled in arms, but I never heard that he was a wizard. And still he must be, for as many men fall there in the back as fall here."

And with that he called off his men, and they rode away, and it was considered a great disgrace that he with so many men could not slay one man, even though that man was Grettir.

Grettir was wounded and worn out with fighting, but he, too, marveled at what had happened, and so he went through the rift, and there, on the far side of it, was another man as large as Grettir and also wounded, leaning against a rock with a sword in his hand. Grettir went up to him and saw that it was Hallmund whom he had met at Kjol and who had first told him that his name was Lopt.

"So it was you who guarded my back," said Grettir.

"I told you that we would meet again," said Hallmund. "I thought I owed you something for the rough way I took my reins away from you up there in the north. I fear I may have bruised your hands."

"You seem to have a few bruises yourself now," said Grettir, looking at his wounds.

"A few," said Hallmund. "But I did not like the odds you faced. They seemed a little long, so I thought I would even them somewhat. Now I think that you should come and stay with me for a while, as I told you that you would when we last met. For time cannot have passed quickly for you here on the heath."

"I will come with you gladly," said Grettir. "And I hope that some day I may have a chance to repay you for the help you gave me."

They mounted their horses, and Hallmund led Grettir to a large cave at the foot of the glacier which men call Balljokull. There they found Hallmund's daughter, a tall and handsome maiden, who exclaimed at the sight of their wounds and scolded them both and then tended them to health again.

Grettir stayed there with Hallmund and his daughter for most of that summer, and while he was there, he made up verses about Hallmund which went in part:

Hallmund strode from his mountain cave
And aid to his friend from Kjol he gave.
To the hut on the heath came the foemen dread
And the prize that they sought was Grettir's head.
Swords flashed in the sun and one by one
The war-fain fell till the fight was done
And they rode away from the rift in the rock
Where around the dead the ravens flocked.
Praise then to Hallmund, like Thor in the fray,
Whose blade gave Grettir his life that day.

As the summer wore on, Grettir found himself yearning to be in the company of men again and, if possible, to see his friends and kinsmen, for it was now more than three years since he had first gone to the heath. Hallmund said that if his need was so great, he should go, but he told Grettir to come and visit him again, and Grettir said he would.

Grettir went west to see Thorsteinn Kuggason, who welcomed him warmly. They talked together about where Grettir might stay next, and Thorsteinn said that Grettir now had so many enemies that there were few, no matter how friendly, who would dare to take him in. But he suggested that Grettir might go south to the marsh country and see how the living was in those parts, and Grettir said he would. So that fall he went there.

19

The Humbling of Gisli

BJORN, known as the Hitdale Warrior, was an important chieftain who lived at Holm, near the marsh country. His great-grandfather and Grettir's great-grandfather, Onund Treefoot, had been comrades. And because of the warm fellowship that there had been between those two early fighting men, Bjorn gave his friendship to Grettir.

Grettir asked him if he would take him in, and Bjorn said what Thorsteinn had said: that Grettir now had so many enemies that this was no light matter.

"But," said Bjorn, "I will help you in every other way that I can on one condition. And that is that you leave my own people in peace."

Grettir said that he would do that, and then Bjorn told him what he had in mind. There was a mountain near Holm that ran north from the marsh country. And on the mountain there was a place, overlooking the high road, that could be easily defended because the approach to it was so steep. It was Bjorn's thought that Grettir should go there and get what he needed to live, either from the folk of the marsh country or from those who passed on the road.

This seemed a good plan to Grettir, and he went to the place of which Bjorn had told him. There he found a hollow that was sheltered on all sides. There were rocks in front of it, and in the rocks there was a cleft through which he could see the road below. He hung heavy gray cloth in front of the cleft so that it was hidden from those who passed on the road. But when he wished, he could draw it aside and look out. He built himself a house in the hollow, and when he began taking his supplies and whatever he needed from those who lived below, the people of the district felt they had a very unwelcome guest among them.

When Grettir had been in his new hiding place for about a year, a trader and sea captain named Gisli landed in a port near the marsh country. He was a big, strong man whose arms and clothes were very showy and who thought very well of himself. He fell into talk with a man named Thord who had lost much property to Grettir and said, "Is it true that you are having a good deal of trouble with an outlaw who lives near here?"

"You must mean Grettir," said Thord. "Yes, we
have been having trouble with him because it has been
hard to find him. But most of us think that is just as
well. For if we did find him, he would not be easy to
deal with."

"He does not frighten me," said Gisli. "I have more
than held my own with much mightier men when I
was campaigning with King Knut in England. I should
like to see what would happen when we faced each
other with swords in our hands."

"If you could do something about him, there would be more than glory in it for you," said Thord. "For there is more money on his head than that of any other outlaw in Iceland."

"How much?" asked Gisli.

"Well, to begin with there were six marks of silver. But this summer Thorir of Gard added another three marks."

"Now I am more interested than ever," said Gisli. "I am going north after my ship is hauled up for the winter, and if you will tell me where I can find this Grettir, we will see whether I am a match for him or not. But I don't want him to be on his guard and avoid me, so let us be quiet about what I plan to do."

Thord said he would tell no one about it, but, as the old saying has it, "Even in the woods a listening ear is near," and friends of Bjorn heard their talk and told Bjorn about it, and Bjorn told Grettir. Grettir smiled but did not say how he would deal with Gisli.

Gisli was delayed after he had hauled his ship up and did not start north until just before winter set in. He had two men with him, and when they came near the mountain, they all put on their best and brightest clothes, for they wanted to attract Grettir's attention.

Grettir was up early that morning, and looking down from his lair, he saw three men riding up from the south. He wondered who they were, but when they came closer and he saw their colorful clothes and inlaid shields, he thought he knew. He felt it would be too bad if Gisli did not have a chance to meet him as he had been so anxious to do, so he took his weapons and went running down the steep hillside.

When Gisli saw him, he said, "Things have worked out just as I had hoped. This must be Grettir. Now we shall have good sport and win much silver besides."

He and his men got off their horses and stood there waiting. Grettir came up to them and took hold of the clothes that Gisli had in his saddlebag, saying, "Though I am a particular man, I often make do with little things. So I will take this."

"No, you will not," said Gisli. "Do you know who I am?"

"It makes little difference to me," said Grettir.

"We shall see whether it makes a difference or not," said Gisli. "Have at him, men."

With that, the three men drew their swords and attacked Grettir. He fell back a few paces so that he had a rock behind him and kept them in play while he studied them. It was soon clear to Grettir that Gisli was not quite so brave as he had claimed, for he let his men do most of the fighting while he urged them on from the rear. Becoming tired of defending himself, Grettir went over to the attack, and almost at once one of the men fell, then the other, and Gisli began giving ground back along the road.

"It seems strange to me," said Grettir, "that one who

has done so well with such mighty men abroad should do so poorly here. For you have been of little help to your companions."

"It was men I had to do with then," said Gisli, "not fiends from Hell."

They exchanged but a few more strokes, then Gisli dropped his sword and shield, turned and ran away along the road. Grettir ran after him, but did not press him too closely. When Gisli saw this, he dropped his cloak, hoping that Grettir would stop to pick it up. But Grettir stayed at his heels. On they ran, along the road and then away from it and down toward the river, Gisli still stripping off his garments one by one and dropping them, and Grettir still coming after him.

When they reached the river, Gisli was worn out with running and had nothing left on him but his shirt.

Grettir seized him and threw him to the ground, saying, "If you are the Gisli who was so anxious to meet Grettir, why have you been trying so hard to avoid him?"

"Because I did not know what manner of man he was," said Gisli. "But now that I do know, I rue the day I first heard his name. Keep my goods, but let me go free."

"If you had listened well, you would have learned what manner of man I am," said Grettir. "But now I must see that you do not forget it." And tearing a branch from a tree, he gave Gisli a sound thrashing.

Leaving him lying there groaning, Grettir returned the way he had come, picking up Gisli's clothes as he went and taking them, his weapons, and his goods back to his eyrie with him.

When Gisli got his strength back, he crossed the river and took shelter in a stead there. Those in the stead guessed from his condition what had happened, and the tale spread from there all through the west of Iceland. Though there were many in those parts who did not love Grettir, few were sorry for what had happened, and most men thought that Gisli had only gotten what he deserved for his boasting.

20

The Last Visit Home and The Journey to Drangey

WHEN Grettir had been on the mountain for three years, there were so many in those parts who were against him because of his raiding that things began to become difficult for Bjorn. For everyone knew that Bjorn was his friend and had counseled and helped him in every way that he could. So Grettir left the district and went again to visit Hallmund.

He stayed with Hallmund and his daughter till the end of summer. Then he became restless, and Hallmund told him of a new place he might try, and that was a hidden valley that lay to the southwest. So Grettir went south and west, and climbed up to the glacier and went along it until he came to the valley. It was long and narrow and shut in on every side by

the ice, but the valley itself was so fair that it was like
a place enchanted. Though it was high up, hot springs
gushed from the earth, and their warmth kept the ice
back, and grass and small trees grew there, and a clear
stream ran down the center of the valley. There were
so many sheep in the valley that Grettir could not
count them, and they were fatter than any he had ever
seen elsewhere.

Grettir built a hut and spent the winter in the valley,
but when spring came, his loneliness and restlessness

were again too much for him, and he spent the summer and the next winter traveling along the eastern fjords. But he found that most men there were against him, too, so he returned to the far west, and after living for a while in the mountains, he rode east to Bjarg.

It was now seventeen years since he had first been exiled for the slaying of Skeggi, and twelve years since he had been unjustly outlawed for the burning of the sons of Thorir of Gard. During those last twelve years he had been home but little. When he arrived at the stead, his mother, Asdis, welcomed him warmly and joyfully, and so did his younger brother, Illugi. Illugi was then fifteen years old, a tall, handsome young man, as much loved by his mother as was Grettir.

"How go things with you, my son?" asked Asdis.

"They go badly, Mother," said Grettir. "The lot of an outlaw, with the hands of most men turned against you, is not easy at best. But as time goes on, the curse that Glam laid upon me grows heavier rather than lighter. While there is no man or anything I fear during the daylight hours, I can now do nothing nor go anywhere after dark because of the things I see. And so, even though it means my life, I can no longer bear to be alone."

"Then you shall not live alone," said his mother. "You shall stay here with us."

"That I cannot do," said Grettir. "For there are too many who hate me and it would only bring trouble to you, even worse trouble than you have already had."

"What will you do then?" she asked. "Where will you go?"

"There is a place to which I could go," he said. "A place of which I have heard and where I would be safer than anywhere else in Iceland."

"Where is that?"

"The island of Drangey," said Grettir. "I heard of it when I was in the north. It is an island in the Skagafjord, some distance from shore. It rises sheer from the waters of the fjord, and no one can get on to it save with ladders. I was told that, once I was there, I would be safe from attack by any number of men as long as the ladders were guarded."

"It sounds like a safe place, but a lonely one," said Asdis.

"It is because it is such a lonely place that I have not gone there before," said Grettir. "I dare not go there unless I can find someone I can truly trust to go there with me. And where shall I find such a man?"

"Need you ask that, brother?" said Illugi. "I will go there with you. I do not know how much help I can be, but trust me you can. I will stand fast with you no matter what happens."

"There is no man I would rather have with me," said Grettir. "For young as you are, there is no one I trust more. But I will not take you with me if our mother does not wish me to."

"It is a hard choice that you give me, Grettir," said Asdis. "I had a husband and three sons. Asmund died, and Atli was slain, and during these past few years, I have had only Illugi. Now you would take him from me, too."

"It is not written in letters carved in stone that he must come with me, Mother," said Grettir.

"But it is, Grettir," said Asdis. "For you are my son, too, and your need is greater than mine. So he will go."

Illugi embraced his mother at this, for like many he thought Grettir to be the bravest man and the greatest hero in the land, and beyond all else he wanted to go and share this adventure with him. They made ready for their journey, Asdis giving them whatever goods and money they needed. And when they left the stead, Asdis went along the road with them a way as she had gone with Grettir when he left to go to Norway for the first time. She was quiet at first, saying nothing, until Grettir said, "Why are you so silent, Mother?"

"Because this is a dark day for me," she said. "It has come to me that I shall never see either of you again."

"Shall we not go then?" asked Grettir.

"Nay, you must go. No man can escape his destiny. You will be safe on Drangey. But many will begrudge your stay there, and in the end that is where your bones will be laid to rest."

"How do you know this, Mother?" asked Illugi.

"Through dreams that I have had. Beware of

treachery. And above all things, guard yourself against witchcraft. For against that even your strength, Grettir, is powerless."

"How one can guard oneself against it I do not know," said Grettir. "But I will try." Then, as she began weeping, he said, "Nay, weep not, Mother. If we are attacked, the world will know that you had men for sons."

With that he embraced her, and so did Illugi, and they said farewell.

Grettir and Illugi went north, staying with kinsmen along the way. Autumn was past, and it was well into winter when they turned eastward toward the head of Skagafjord. There, on a cold and snowy day, they met a tall, thin, poorly dressed man with a huge head. He asked them who they were, and they told him, and he said his name was Glaum. He was a vagabond who did not like to work and who wandered about the district, living in any way that he could. He kept staring at Grettir, for in spite of the cold and wind and snow, Grettir had the hood of his cloak thrown back and was bareheaded, as he always was no matter what the weather. This Glaum kept larking about, making jokes and telling them the gossip of the district, and finally he asked Grettir whether they could not use a man to work for them. For, he said, he would like to go with them.

"You sound to me like a man who likes company,"

said Grettir. "And there will be little of that where we are going."

"All the more reason why you should want me with you," said Glaum. "For while I am around, you need never fear that things will be too quiet for you."

Since Glaum means the loud or noisy one, Grettir laughed at this and said it was a fitting name and, if Glaum wished, he could come with them.

They went on till they came to a large farm on the shore of the fjord near the island. The farmer gave them shelter, but he frowned when Grettir told him they wanted to go out to Drangey and asked him if he would take them there. He said that the island belonged to some of the most important men around Skagafjord and that they would not like the idea. He stopped frowning, however, and his eyes widened when Grettir took out the purse that his mother had given him, and after thinking about it, he changed his mind and said he would do as Grettir wished.

He told three of his men to get the boat ready and take Grettir, Illugi, and Glaum out to the island that night. It was a clear, moonlit night, and as they drew close to Drangey, Grettir saw that it was everything he had been told it was. It was near the center of the fjord, about a mile from the nearest point on the shore. And although it was not a large island, it was covered with grass, and about eighty sheep, belonging to farmers in the district, grazed there. Sea birds nested

on many parts on it, particularly on a crag at one end.
But, most important, while there were a few shallow
beaches, most of the island rose sheer from the water
and the cliffs were too steep and high to climb except
by ladders.

The farmer's men rowed Grettir and his companions
to the place where the ladders were. There was one
that led up to a narrow ledge. And on the ledge was a
second, even longer ladder that led from there to the
top of the cliffs.

Grettir, Illugi, and Glaum climbed the ladders and walked about, exploring the island and picking out a sheltered spot where they would build themselves a hut.

And so began Grettir's stay on Drangey which he had been told was the safest refuge in Iceland. And so it was to be for several years. But in the end, because of the enmity of one man and the cunning of an old woman, it was to be the place where he would die.

21

Grettir on Drangey and at the Thing

WHILE the farmer's men were rowing Grettir, Illugi, and Glaum out to Drangey, they told them that the island belonged to some twenty land-owners who lived in those parts. They all had some share in it, but the largest share belonged to two bro-thers named Hjalti and Thorbjorn Angle.

Hjalti was an important chieftain and was well liked, but Thorbjorn Angle was not liked at all. He was a big, strong, one-eyed man with a fierce temper. His temper was so bad that once when he got into a quarrel with his stepmother and she struck him, he beat her so badly that she never recovered from it and finally died. Thorbjorn left home after that, going to live in Vidvik, and became a complete ruffian.

Grettir, Illugi, and Glaum settled down on Drangey and found life there pleasant. They built a hut out of logs and driftwood in the spot they had picked out when they arrived. For food they had the sheep that had been left there to graze and sea birds' eggs and fish, which were plentiful in the waters of the fjord.

Since the island was some distance from the nearest settlement and most of the steads on the fjord, none knew that they were living there except the farmer and his men, and they told no one about it. Shortly after midwinter, Hjalti, Thorbjorn Angle, and all the others who shared in the ownership of Drangey manned a boat and went out to get the sheep they had left there.

When they came close to the island, they saw men moving about on top of the cliffs. They were surprised at this, but they thought that perhaps a ship had been wrecked in the fjord and the sailors had come ashore on Drangey. However, when they rowed around to where they usually landed, they found that the ladders had been pulled up. Now they began to suspect that something was wrong and they called out to those on the island and asked them who they were. Grettir told them, and then those in the boat asked who had brought them out there.

"Whoever he was, it is clear that he was more our friend than yours," said Grettir, for he had promised the farmer that he would not tell anyone that it was he who had helped them.

"Let us have our sheep," said those in the boat, "and we will take you ashore with us in peace and say nothing about the animals you have already eaten."

"Now that is a generous offer," said Grettir, "and one that does you credit. But I would not put you to so much trouble. So let us each keep what we already have."

"But we have nothing," said those in the boat, "while you have both the island and our sheep. Do not play games with us and anger us, or it will go hard with you."

"Since I fear you not, why should I fear your anger?" said Grettir. "If you know aught about me, you should know that I never give up what I already have."

Then those in the boat tried speaking fair words to him, offering him money to leave the island. But Grettir would have none of this either, and finally those in the boat gave up and rowed back to land and told everyone into whose hands the island had fallen. And though they spent much time that winter talking about it, they could think of no way in which they could get Grettir and his companions to leave Drangey.

The days passed until it was spring, and men in those parts began to assemble for their local Thing. Grettir heard about this from the farmer who was their friend, for it was his custom always to be on the best of terms with those who lived near him, and he said this would be a good time to go ashore and get supplies. Illugi did not like this idea, but he could do nothing with Grettir. So Grettir put on his oldest and shabbiest clothes as a disguise, and telling Illugi and Glaum to guard the ladders well, he had the farmer's men take him ashore.

Grettir soon got together all the supplies he wanted, and then since life on the island had been so quiet, he decided to go to the Thing. He arrived just as all were leaving the law courts and sat down on a rock with his hood pulled forward to cover his face and waited to see what would happen.

Since it was a warm and pleasant day, men now began to play games and contest with one another in wrestling. There were two brothers at the Thing, both named Thord, who were bigger and stronger than any in those parts. They were the best of all in the games that were played. But it was Thorbjorn Angle who was foremost in arranging things. He told everyone where to go and what to do, taking men by the shoulders and pushing or pulling them about until they had done as he said.

The wrestling was begun by the youngest men and those who were least strong, and there was good sport in that. But when it came time for someone to wrestle with the brothers Thord, no one could be found to stand up to them. Then, looking around, Thorbjorn Angle saw a big man sitting on a rock, his face shadowed by his hood. He went up to him and tried to pull him to his feet, but he was unable to move him.

"No one today has held so firm against me," said Thorbjorn. "What is your name?"

"You can call me Gest," said the man.

"Well, you are a welcome guest," said Thorbjorn. "Will you join our games? We have two men here with whom no one will wrestle."

"That might be good sport for you, but not for me," said the man. "I have not done any wrestling in some time."

"I give you my word that they will not be too rough with you," said Thorbjorn.

"That eases my mind somewhat," said the man. "And I might do it if you give me your word about something else."

"What is that?"

"That no matter what happens you grant me peace here at the Thing until such time as I return home."

All at the Thing said that they would do so, and one man came forward and pledged peace, and all there gave their word that they would abide by the pledge.

"Since I take you to be honorable men," said Gest, "I will now do as you wish." And he threw back his hood and stripped off his upper garments, and when he had done so, a great silence came over all there for they knew that this was Grettir.

For a moment they looked at him; then they began whispering among themselves, and some said that a pledge to an outlaw was no pledge at all, and others said that it mattered not to whom it was given: an oath was sacred.

"You have as much at stake here as I have," said Grettir. "For while my life hangs in the balance, your honor is involved. So instead of whispering among yourselves, why do you not speak plainly and tell me what is in your minds?"

"I will speak," said Hjalti, Thorbjorn Angle's brother. "And I say that though you have tricked us into giving you peace, we will still abide by our pledge, for we are indeed honorable men and not oath breakers."

At this all said that he had spoken well and agreed that they would abide by their pledge of peace. But Thorbjorn Angle said nothing, for he felt that he had been made to look a fool and he could not forget that Grettir was keeping him from his property by holding Drangey.

Then Grettir went forward for wrestling, and one of the Thord brothers was picked to go against him. He rushed at Grettir and tried to overset him, but he could not move him. And while he strained at him, Grettir took hold of him and threw him backward over his head, so that he fell on his shoulders, and that was a great fall.

Then the folk asked Grettir whether he would wrestle both brothers at once, and he said if they wished it, he would. So now both Thord brothers came at Grettir together, and there was a mighty struggle. But even together the brothers could do nothing with Grettir, for he always had one or the other down on his back or his knees, though even he could not put them both down at the same time.

When they were finally spent and weary and called a halt to the wrestling, everyone thanked them for the sport they had given them and said that though each of the Thord brothers was as strong as two strong men, both together were no stronger than Grettir alone.

As Grettir prepared to leave the Thing, all those who owned shares in Drangey came up to him and asked him again if he would not give up the island. But he said he would not, for while he stayed there, he was safe and there were not many such places in Iceland.

Then Grettir returned to Drangey, and Illugi rejoiced to see him for he had been much concerned about him. And when Grettir told him where he had been and what had happened, Illugi scolded him for taking such risks, but he agreed that the folk of Skagafjord had indeed behaved most honorably in keeping their pledge to Grettir.

22

Thorbjorn Angle's Visit to Drangey and Grettir's Second Visit to the Mainland

AFTER Grettir's visit to the Thing, the least wealthy of those who owned shares in Drangey began to talk among themselves. And since it was clear that they would get no use out of the island, they now offered to sell their shares to Hjalti and Thorbjorn Angle. But Hjalti would not buy them, for the landowners made it part of the bargain that whoever bought their shares must either kill Grettir or get him to leave Drangey, and he did not think that either of these things could be done. Thorbjorn Angle, however, thought that it could be accomplished by sleights and trickery if not in any other way. So he said he would undertake to deal with Grettir if he were well paid for it. Whereupon Hjalti gave up his share of the island to him, and many of the landowners sold their shares to him for a very low price. In this way Thorbjorn Angle got the greater part of the ownership of the island for very little silver, but at the same time he bound himself to rid Skagafjord of Grettir.

When summer was ending, Thorbjorn Angle manned a boat and went out to Drangey, and Grettir, Illugi, and Glaum came to the edge of the cliffs to hear what he had to say. Thorbjorn asked Grettir if there was any way he could persuade him to leave the island, and Grettir said it was not likely that he could.

"But you do not say no without any doubt," said Thorbjorn, "and that is good. For as things stand now, I would give you more than anyone has yet offered you if you will leave."

"How is that?" asked Grettir.

"Because most of those who owned shares in the island have either given or sold them to me. So it is worth much to me to get you to go."

"Say you so?" said Grettir. "Then if ever I thought of going, I will think of it no longer. I was not happy at the thought that all the men of Skagafjord were against me. But now that it is only you whom I am keeping from his property, it troubles me not at all, for I like you no more than you like me. And so you may save yourself further journeys here, because for my part the matter is settled and I will not go."

"All things must come to an end," said Thorbjorn. "Even my patience. And that will be an evil day for you."

"I have lived through days more evil than any you can bring me," said Grettir.

Then Thorbjorn told his men to put about and row back home, and that ended their parley.

By this time Grettir, Illugi, and Glaum had been on Drangey for two years and had eaten most of the sheep. There was one ram, however, which they would not kill. They called him Graybelly, for he was gray below, and he was so tame that he would follow them everywhere and come to the hut at night and knock on the door with his horns to be let in. Even without the sheep they still had plenty to eat, for there were always the birds which nested on the island, and their eggs, and the fish that they caught. However, firewood was not always easy to come by, and Glaum's chief work was to watch for logs and driftwood and bring it up to the hut. Since he had to carry the wood up the ladders, he began to tire of this and grumble and get careless. It was also his duty to tend the fire at night. And though Grettir had told him to watch it well, for they had no boat and no way of getting more fire, one night he let it go out.

Grettir was very angry at this and took a stick to beat Glaum, but Glaum said that if he had known what a hard life he was to have on Drangey, he would never have come there. For he was not only cut off from all men, living the life of an outlaw, but now he was to be blamed and beaten when something went wrong.

Since, apart from his grumbling and general slack-
ness, this was the first time that Glaum had failed them
in a matter that was truly serious, Grettir said he would
not beat him and asked Illugi what he thought they
should do. Illugi said he did not think there was anything they could do except wait for the farmer to come
out to the island and ask him to bring them some fire.

"We might have to wait a long time for that," said
Grettir. "And, in the meantime, our life would be hard
indeed with the weather so cold and getting colder. I
think I will see if I cannot swim to land."

"I beg you not to try it," said Illugi. "It is much too
far, and the water is too cold. And if anything should
happen to you, that would be the end for Glaum and
me also."

"I shall not drown," said Grettir. "It is in my mind
that when I die it shall be in another way." And Illugi
could not persuade him not to go.

At dusk Grettir stripped to his breeches and dived
into the fjord. Though it was cold, the weather was
fair and the current was with him, and swimming
strongly, Grettir reached the shore shortly after dark.
He went into the hall of the farmer's stead and found
that all there were asleep. And since he was weary from
his swim and the hall was warm, he stretched out near
the fire and went to sleep also.

He was still sleeping in the morning when the farmer's daughter and one of the serving maids came into

the hall. Though she had never seen him before, the serving maid said, "As I hope for salvation, mistress, this can only be the outlaw, Grettir."

Grettir opened his eyes at this and said, "I am indeed Grettir. What will you do about it?"

"I will do and say nothing," she said, for now that she had seen him, she found much to admire about him.

"Then may you have the salvation you hoped for," said Grettir. "For you are not only wise, but you are as good as you are fair." And picking her up, he gave her an embrace that was like to have cracked her ribs, and kissed her soundly. Then, lest the farmer's daughter be jealous, he embraced and kissed her, too.

The farmer himself came into the hall soon after that, and Grettir told him how and why he had come there. The farmer said that this was a great feat that he had done, and he brought out his boat and took Grettir back to the island with the fire he needed.

When it became known that Grettir had swum a full sea mile to the mainland in that cold weather, all thought that there was no one like him for prowess both on land and sea. But those of Skagafjord who had sold their shares in the island to Thorbjorn Angle spoke hard words to him for not having gotten rid of Grettir and wanted their shares back again, Thorbjorn, however, said that though the task was not an easy one, he still hoped to bring it about and asked them to be patient yet awhile.

23

Haering at Drangey
and What Happened
at the Thing

THAT summer a ship came to Skagafjord with a young man aboard named Haering. He was very sure-footed and agile and such a great climber that it was said there was no rock or cliff he could not scale. He went to visit Thorbjorn Angle, and while he was staying with him, he heard how Grettir was holding Drangey. He then began to ask Thorbjorn to take him out there so that he could look at the cliffs and see whether they were too high and steep for him to climb. Thorbjorn did not need much urging and told Haering that if he could get up them and kill Grettir, he would be well rewarded for it.

So one day they sailed out to Drangey, and Thorbjorn put Haering ashore on the far side of the island

and then went around to where the ladders were and began a conversation with Grettir. Thorbjorn asked him again whether he could persuade him to leave the island, and Grettir said he had told him that he could not.

"You have been playing games with us for some time now," said Thorbjorn. "But they cannot go on forever. They must come to an end one day."

"All things bide their day," said Grettir. "And all must come to an end in time."

"Then do you not fear our wrath when that day comes and you can hold us off no longer?"

"In all my life there has only been one thing that I have ever feared," said Grettir, "and it is not you or any man born of woman."

While they were talking, Haering had been climbing the cliff on the far side of the island. And such was his skill that he reached the top without the help of a ladder or a rope from above, something no man had been able to do before. Grettir and Illugi were still engaged with Thorbjorn and those in the boat, and had their backs to him, so Haering drew his ax from his belt and crept toward them.

At that moment Illugi turned and saw him and said to Grettir, "There is a man on the island. A stranger."

"What sort of man?" asked Grettir.

"Since he is hurrying this way with his ax raised high, I do not think he is a friend."

"So now we know why Thorbjorn came here this time," said Grettir. "It seems that he wished to have his turn at playing games. Do you deal with our visitor while I keep watch here and see whether the others down below there have anything more in mind."

"With pleasure, brother," said Illugi. And drawing his sword, he went to meet Haering.

Young though he was, Illugi was Grettir's brother, and there was that in the way he looked and carried himself which made Haering pause. Then, as Illugi came on, sword in hand, Haering turned and fled. Like one pursued by trolls he ran, with Illugi coming ever behind him. Reaching the end of the island, Haering looked back and, seeing Illugi still coming after him, he leaped, hoping to gain the safety of the waters of the fjord. But his skill in this was not equal to his skill in climbing, and he fell short, landing on the rocks below, and so got his death.

"How fares it with our guest?" asked Grettir when Illugi returned to where he waited.

"Not well," said Illugi. "He would not wait to let me greet him, but took his leave by leaping. And now I fear he will never climb or leap again."

When Thorbjorn Angle heard this, he told his men to put about and row back to shore.

"Twice have I come to talk to Grettir," he said. "It may be that I will come again. And if I do, I pledge my word that he will not remain here much longer."

Then Thorbjorn returned home, and Grettir and his companions remained undisturbed on Drangey all that winter. But though Grettir knew it not, during that time his fortunes suffered two hard blows. For during the winter Skapti the Lawman died, and in the spring Snorri the Godi died also. These two were among the most important men in Iceland, men whose word carried the greatest weight at the All-Thing because of their position and their knowledge of the law. They were both supporters of Grettir—Skapti because he was kin of Grettir's, and Snorri because he had always been a friend of Grettir's family and because he admired Grettir himself. They had expected to do what they could to have the sentence of outlawry against him lifted at the Thing that was to take place during the next summer. But now their help was lost to Grettir.

When the assembly took place at the All-Thing that summer, Steinn, the son of Thorgest, was appointed Lawman in Skapti's place. He was a wise and fair man, and Grettir's friends came to him and asked for his opinion on their case, which was as follows:

It was now twenty years since Grettir had been declared an outlaw for the first time for the slaying of Skeggi. It was the claim of Grettir's friends that twenty years was the longest sentence of outlawry that could be given to any man, and that since Grettir had completed that term, the sentence should now be lifted.

Grettir's enemies, led by Thorir of Gard, disputed this. They said that during the time that Grettir was an outlaw he had done many things which in themselves deserved to be punished by outlawry, and that therefore the sentence against him should be longer than twenty years. When Steinn the Lawman did not agree with them, Thorir of Gard came forward with a new obstacle. He said that in the twenty years since Grettir had first been declared an outlaw, there was one year when he had not been one. That was the year when he had returned from Norway for the first time and before he went there on the journey during which Thorir's sons had been burned to death. Therefore, said, Thorir, he had not been an outlaw for twenty years, but only for nineteen years.

Since Thorir of Gard was an influential man with strong supporters, Steinn allowed this claim. But he said that no man could be outlawed for more than twenty years in all, no matter what he had done in the meantime. So it seemed certain that if Grettir could endure until the following summer, the sentence against him would be removed, and he could again live the life of a free man.

There were many who were not pleased at the thought that in a year Grettir would go free, and among them were the men of Skagafjord. They went to Thorbjorn Angle and told him he had not kept his agreement with them. They had sold him their shares of the island for very little on condition that he kill Grettir or drive him away, and he had not done either of these things. Therefore, they said, he must either deal with Grettir at once or return their shares of the island to them.

Their reasons for taking this position were not hard for most men to understand. In the first place, if Grettir were freed of his sentence and left Drangey of his own free will, Thorbjorn would have gotten the ownership of the island for little money and would have done nothing to deserve it. Thus he would have outwitted his neighbors, getting the better of them in a bargain, and no man likes that. But there was another reason, too. Thorbjorn was a man who was much disliked by all in Skagafjord. Behind their willingness to sell him their shares in the island on condition that he kill Grettir was their hope that, in trying to do so, it would be Thorbjorn and not Grettir who would be killed. And that was why, with time running out, they pressed him all the harder.

Thorbjorn, however, did not want to give up the island. So he asked for a little more time, and in his great need he called in an ally whom even he had been unwilling to call on until then.

24

Thurid the Witch at Drangey

THORBJORN Angle had a foster mother named Thurid. She was quite old now and did little, but when she was young she had been greatly skilled in witchcraft and magic, knowing all manner of spells. She had practiced her lore in the days before the land became Christian, but made little use of her skills afterward. This was not because it was forbidden by law to sacrifice or perform other heathen rites—for it was not, as long as these rites were performed in private—it was because, with the coming of Christianity, there were few who still believed in the power of the ancient knowledge.

Since all of Thorbjorn's plots against Grettir had come to naught, however, and since his need was great, he now went to Thurid and asked her if she would help him.

"As the old saying has it," she said, " 'Where does one go for wool but to the goat house?' It is a goat house to which few come these days, but it is clear to me why you have come. It is a hard thing to think one-self above all other men, and then to fail when it comes to the test."

"It is true that I have been able to do nothing with Grettir," said Thorbjorn. "Therefore will you not help me?"

"Though I am infirm and can scarce rise from my bed, I will help you," she said. "But only if what is done is done as I say."

Thorbjorn said it would be as she wished, and she said she would tell him when the time was right. On a fair day near the end of summer she said, "The weather is now settled, and the sea is calm. Take me out to Drangey so that I may see this Grettir."

"Do not ask that of me, foster mother," said Thor-bjorn. "Each time that I have gone out there things have fared worse with me than the last."

"You said that all would be as I wished," said Thurid. "If you do not do as I say, I will not help you. I must see this Grettir for myself. Only then can I tell whether his fortune waxes or wanes, and whether I can do aught against him."

"If you will have it so, we will go," said Thorbjorn.

"I have said that I might go there again, and that if I did, he would not remain there much longer."

"Much pain and trouble will we both have before Grettir is laid in the earth," said Thurid. "And it will go even harder with you afterward, for his death will lead to yours. But you have bound yourself to deal with him and so we must go there."

Then Thorbjorn had his boat manned and went aboard her with eleven of his men. Thurid went aboard her also and lay in the stern covered with rugs and clothes so that she could not be seen. The boat was rowed out to Drangey, and when Grettir and Illugi saw it coming, they went to the place where the ladders were, to hear what Thorbjorn had to say to them.

Thorbjorn said he had come once more to hear whether he could persuade Grettir to leave the island in peace.

"I have told you many times," said Grettir, "that I will not leave, but mean to stay here no matter what happens."

"Now do I truly know with what manner of men I have to deal," said Thorbjorn. "You are not men of middle-earth, but men from Hel's realm. It will be many days before I come here again."

"I would not count it as one of my griefs if you never came again," said Grettir.

Then Thurid stirred and put aside the rugs and clothes that covered her and said, "You have spoken truly when you said what manner of men these were, Thorbjorn. You have made them fair offerings, and they have spurned them, and there are few things that lead more surely to evil than to refuse what is good. Now I say this to you, Grettir. From this time forward your health, your luck, and your wisdom will all become less and less, and your days even blacker than they have been in the past."

Grettir started violently at this and said, "Who is the fiend who is there in the boat with Thorbjorn?"

"I think she must be Thurid, Thorbjorn's foster mother," said Illugi. "I have heard our friend, the farmer, talk of her."

"Well, curse the hag!" said Grettir. "Her eyes swim like Glam's, and her words have the same fateful ring! I know that her spells will bring evil to us, but she shall not escape scatheless. She shall have something to remind her of her journey here."

Picking up a huge rock, Grettir hurled it. And though the boat was farther from the island than Thorbjorn had thought any man could throw, it struck the heap of clothes in the stern. Whereupon Thurid screamed loudly, for it had broken her thighbone.

"I wish you had not done that," said Illugi.

"Blame me not for doing it, but for not doing more," said Grettir. "For her life would have been little enough to pay for both of ours."

"If it comes to that," said Illugi, "I hope that our

lives will not go so cheaply, but will cost that of many others besides that of an old witch."

"Yet it is she whom I fear," said Grettir. "Our mother warned us to beware of witchcraft. But even if she had not, I would still remember that it was after Glam's curse that my life changed and became hard and bitter."

Thorbjorn's men, meanwhile, had begun rowing back to shore.

"Things have gone as I thought they would," said Thorbjorn to his foster mother. "We have gained little glory by this journey, and you have received an injury that will last you for the rest of your life."

"It has not gone quite so badly as you think," said Thurid. "From this time onward, their fortunes will fade. As for me, I care not whether I live or die so long as I have my vengeance for what Grettir did to me."

"Stern is the stuff of which you are made, foster mother," said Thorbjorn. "Perhaps more enduring than was your leg."

When they arrived home, Thurid took to her bed and lay there for nearly a month before her broken leg had healed enough for her to walk again. Men laughed much at what had happened and said that Thorbjorn had had little luck in his dealings with Grettir. For there had been first the pledge of peace at the Thing, then the death of Haering, and now the

breaking of Thurid's thigh. But while Thorbjorn
did not like their laughter, he took heart from his
foster mother's words, believing that forces were
now at work which would undo Grettir.

Meanwhile, on Drangey, Grettir's night fears
returned and became more troublesome than ever.
Often Illugi would awake and find Grettir sitting by
the fire and say, "What ails you, brother?"

"Nothing," Grettir would answer.

"The ladders are drawn up, so we need not fear an
attack from Thorbjorn Angle."

"It is not him or anything human that I fear."

"That I know. I will go outside and look about."

Then Illugi would go outside, and when he
returned, he would say, "There is naught stirring
anywhere."

"Thank you, brother," Grettir would say. Then he
would lie down and sleep. But there was no peace for
him there. As he had when he was on the heath, he
would seem to see eyes all about him. But now they
were Thurid's eyes as well as Glam's, and they were
in the sea all about him, rising and falling with the
waves. They would mount higher and higher, this sea
of gleaming eyes, until they were able to overwhelm
the whole island, and then he would awake with a cry.
Though Illugi would talk to him when this happened,
trying to reassure him, there would be no more sleep
for Grettir that night.

25

The Casting of the Spell

AUTUMN passed, and three weeks before winter began, Thurid asked Thorbjorn to take her down to the fjord.

"What will you do there?" asked Thorbjorn.

"A small thing," she said. "Yet it may be that it will lead to a greater one."

Thorbjorn and several of his men carried her to the fjord and set her down. At once, as if she had known where it was, she went limping up the shore to where a tree stump lay near the water's edge. It was large —as big as one man could carry—and gnarled and twisted. She studied it, then told Thorbjorn to turn it over. The underside was smooth and looked as if it had been burned. Taking out a knife, she cut runes on the smooth part, and pricking her finger, reddened them with blood. Then, going backwards and widdershins around it, she began muttering a spell; strange witch words that none could understand save at the end when she bade it go to Drangey and hurt Grettir as he had hurt her.

When she had finished, she told Thorbjorn to push it into the sea. He did so, and though the wind was blowing down the fjord from the north, the stump moved up the fjord against the wind toward Drangey. Thorbjorn watched it go and looked sharply at Thurid. For much as he hated Grettir, he liked not witchcraft: not because he was a church-going man, but because he knew that those who deal with dark powers usually pay for it in the end. He said nothing about it, however, but bade his men pick up Thurid and carry her back home.

The day after Thurid had worked her magic, Grettir and Illugi went down the ladders and began walking around the narrow beach at the foot of the cliffs to look for firewood. When they reached the western side of the island, they came on the tree stump stranded on the shingle, and Illugi said, "Here is a fine bit of firewood, brother. Let us take it back to the hut."

But Grettir kicked it, saying: "It comes from an evil tree. It was sent by evil, and is steeped in evil.

Leave it alone. We shall look elsewhere for wood."

He pushed the stump out into the fjord and told Illugi to beware of it and not to bring it to the hut, for it was sent there for their destruction. Then they went back to the hut, but they said nothing about it to Glaum.

The next day they went looking for firewood again, and behold, there was the tree stump on the beach again, nearer to the ladders than it had been the day before.

"Can you see now that it was not chance that brought it here?" asked Grettir. And Illugi said it could well be that there was witchcraft in it. Again Grettir pushed the stump out into the fjord, and they went on along the beach.

A few days later bad weather set in with wind and rain, and Grettir told Glaum to go out and search for wood. Glaum grumbled loudly, saying that his lot was hard that he had to go out in such foul weather when even the birds sat close in their nests. He went down the ladders, and there he found the tree stump. Counting himself lucky to have had to go no farther, he struggled up the ladders with it, and when he reached the hut, he threw it down outside.

Hearing the noise, Grettir said, "For once Glaum seems to have brought something home." And taking his wood ax, he went out to him.

"I have done my part, now you do yours," said

Glaum. "And may you have as much joy in cutting it up as I had in bringing it here."

It was murky out, and Grettir was angry at Glaum for speaking to him in this way, so without looking at the stump, he raised his ax with both hands and brought it down. But the ax did not bite. Instead, it glanced off and cut deep into Grettir's leg just above the knee.

Then Grettir saw what it was that Glaum had brought home and said, "Now have those who meant me evil finally prevailed, nor will this end the evil. Twice did I reject this stump, but still it found its way here. You, too, have already brought disaster to us twice, Glaum. First, when you let the fire go out, and now again when you bore this accursed thing to our door. If you fail us again, it will be your death as well as ours."

Illugi came out and helped Grettir into the hut and bound up the wound. It bled but little, and Grettir slept well that night. Three days passed, and when they took off the bandages, the wound had closed and seemed almost healed.

"I do not think this wound will trouble you for long," said Illugi.

"I have suffered much worse ones and feared them less," said Grettir. "For there is too much that is strange about these happenings, and ill from ill cometh."

A few nights later Illugi woke and heard Grettir tossing and asked him what was wrong, and Grettir said that his leg was hurting more than it ever had before. They fetched a light and unbound the wound and found that the leg was all swollen and had turned as dark as coal.

"I like not the look of it," said Illugi.

"No more than I liked the look of the witchwoman in the boat," said Grettir. "This wound is of her sending."

"I told you I wished you had not cast that stone at her," said Illugi.

"It matters not," said Grettir. "That which is boded will be." Then he spoke a verse:

Sharp steel have I stood against,
And many foemen buried.
The sea I challenged, and wild beasts,
And mocked the berserk's fury.
Despite Glam's curse, my strength was still
Full as the flood tide's running.
Now here I lie awaiting death
Undone by a witch's cunning.

"It may not come to that, brother," said Illugi.

"It is an end to which we must all come some day," said Grettir, "though I had hoped to die differently, with a sword in my hand. Yet even if our mother had not warned us, I should have foreseen that it would be witchcraft that would end my life, even as it was witchcraft that changed it and brought my years of ill fortune."

"You are still strong," said Illugi. "Perhaps you can fight the poison in your blood."

"I will fight it, as I have fought all else, for as long

as I can," said Grettir. "Meanwhile we must be ever on our guard, for Thorbjorn Angle will not leave matters as they are. You, Glaum, must watch the ladders every day and pull them up every night. If you do not, it will not only cost us our lives, but it will cost you yours, too."

Glaum promised that he would do this faithfully. But now the weather worsened, and the wind shifted to the northeast and blew hard. It became very cold, and Glaum began to grumble at having to stand guard.

"Do you think men are so anxious to take your life," he asked Grettir, "that they will risk their own to come out here in this weather?"

"You are one who will always find some reason for not doing what you do not want to do," said Grettir. "But whether you want to or not, you will still watch the ladders."

And though Glaum continued to grumble, they drove him out every morning to stand guard, and every evening when he came in, Grettir asked him if the ladders were drawn up. And so time passed until it was two weeks since Grettir had gotten his wound. Illugi sat with him day and night, paying no heed to anything else but tending him as best he could. But there was little he could do, for the whole leg was swollen and festering both above and below the wound. And now Illugi, too, began to think that it was a wound that could be Grettir's death.

26

The Deaths of Grettir
and Illugi

About a week after Thurid had cast her spell, she came to see Thorbjorn and asked him if he was not going to visit Grettir again.

"There is nothing I want to do less," he said. Then looking at the way she leaned on her stick, for her leg still pained her, he said, "But do you want to see him again, foster mother?"

"There is no need for me to see him," she said. "I have sent him my greeting, and by now I think he has received it. But if you still wish to get the better of him, you had better go at once to Drangey."

"Each trip I have made there has brought me more shame than the last," said Thorbjorn, "and I am not going again. But even if I wished to go, how could I in this wild weather?"

"Having done what I have done, do you think I can not deal with the gale that is now blowing? You came to me for counsel, and now I will give it to you. Get together as many men as you can, and then go see your brother-in-law, Halldor of Hof, and ask him for help."

It came to Thorbjorn that Thurid might know more about what was happening on Drangey than he had thought, so he sent out a call for men. Most of those who had owned shares in the island would do nothing to help him, saying that dealing with Grettir was his affair. But his brother, Hjalti, sent him three men and others sent him three more. Thorbjorn had six men of his own, so there were twelve with him in all when he rode to Hof to see his brother-in-law, Halldor.

Halldor asked him how things went in his dealings with Grettir, and Thorbjorn told him everything that had happened.

"No good will come of this," said Halldor. "Your foster mother is a witch, and witchcraft is now forbidden."

"That may be," said Thorbjorn. "But there is nothing that I will not do to bring this matter to an end. How shall I get out to Drangey?"

"It seems to me," said Halldor, "that you are counting on something about which I know nothing and in which I have no faith. But if it is a boat you want,

I will get you one. If Grettir is as well as he has always been, then you will accomplish no more with this journey than with your others."

"And if he is not well?"

"Then be wary and hold your hand. For if you do not kill him in fair and open combat, there are many who will avenge him. And, above all else, do not kill Illugi if it can be avoided. For he is not an outlaw like Grettir and has no enemies."

Halldor then gave Thorbjorn six men, and sent him to see a friend of his who had a boat. The friend was not anxious to help them, but said he would do so for Halldor's sake. However he told them they were mad to try to sail to Drangey in such weather, even in his boat, which was much larger than Thorbjorn's. When Thorbjorn insisted, he went down to the boathouse with them and helped them launch the boat.

They hoisted the sail and put out, and as soon as they were well under way, the wind died down somewhat, and they made the passage to Drangey with no trouble, arriving there just as it was getting dark.

Meanwhile Grettir had become so ill that he could no longer rise from his bed. Illugi would not leave him, so it fell to Glaum to stand guard. That morning, though he grumbled more than ever at having to go out in such weather, they sent him out to watch

at the ladders. Telling himself that there was no need
to draw them up, he took shelter behind a rock,
covered himself with his cloak, and went to sleep.
He was still sleeping when Thorbjorn and those with
him reached the island.

Seeing the ladders down and no one moving about
on top of the cliffs, Thorbjorn said, "Things are
different from the way they have ever been before.
It may be that we will be able to do more than we
thought. Let us be resolute and act quickly."

He led them up the ladders, and when they got
to the top of the cliffs, they found Glaum snoring
under his cloak. Recognizing him, Thorbjorn struck
him with the hilt of his sword to awaken him and
said, "Truly I could not wish worse to any man
than that he should trust his life to your keeping."

Glaum stared about wildly and opened his mouth to shout, but Thorbjorn put his sword to his throat and said, "Be silent! Now answer my questions, or I will kill you. Why are the brothers not about?"

"Because Grettir is so sick that he is close to death, and Illugi will not leave him."

"How is that?" asked Thorbjorn.

Then Glaum told him about Grettir's wound and how each day it had worsened, and Thorbjorn laughed, saying, "It seems my foster mother did her work well. As for you, Glaum, true is the old saying that 'Ill it is if a thrall is thine only friend.' For shamefully have you betrayed your master."

And all that were with Thorbjorn said the same, and they beat Glaum so soundly that he fell down almost senseless. Then they went to the hut, and finding the door shut and barred, they knocked loudly on it.

Thinking it was the tame ram who was their pet, Illugi said, "Here is Graybelly knocking to get in."

"If it is Graybelly, he is knocking very hard," said Grettir. "Much too hard."

At that, Illugi seized his sword and shield, and ran to the door just as those outside broke it down. Standing just inside, Illugi defended the doorway so stoutly that none could come in, and when they thrust at him with spears, he smote at them and cut off the spearheads.

Seeing that they could not gain entrance to the hut in that way, they climbed up on to the roof and began to tear off the thatch. With great effort Grettir got to his feet, and catching up a spear, he drove it between the rafters. It struck one of Halldor's men and pierced him through.

After that they were more careful, and they finally broke the roof beams, making a hole large enough for all to jump through. Grettir was on his knees now, unable to rise to his feet again. But his sword—the famous sword he had taken from the howe at Haramsey—was in his hand. One of Hjalti's men was the first to leap down and Grettir smote at him. And it was such a mighty blow that it cut him from shoulder to hip. But in falling, he fell on Grettir and, before Grettir could free his sword arm, Thorbjorn came up behind him and gave him a great wound between the shoulders.

" 'Bare is back without brother behind it'," said Grettir.

Hearing this, Illugi ran to him and, raising his shield in front of Grettir, he defended him so valiantly that all drew back and for a moment gave over the attack.

"Who told you that this was the time to come at us?" asked Grettir.

"What does it matter who told me?" said Thorbjorn.

"It matters not," said Grettir. "Except that I know

it was that accursed hag, your foster mother. May
she burn in Hell for it!"

"Whether it was she or another, the end will be
the same," said Thorbjorn.

Then he and those with him returned to the attack.
And though Illugi continued to fight so bravely that

all said that they had never seen his like, Thorbjorn
and the others made a shield wall and pressed in upon
him until they bore him down. Thus they took him
prisoner. But in the battle he had wounded most of
the attackers and killed three.

They went up to Grettir, who had fallen forward

on his face, and found that he was already dead from the festering of the wound on his leg and the one that Thorbjorn had given him.

Grettir's sword was still in his hand, and Thorbjorn said he had carried it long enough and tried to take it from him. But even in death Grettir's fingers gripped the hilt so tightly that none could loosen them.

"Why should we spare an outlaw?" said Thorbjorn. "Lay his hand on that log."

They did so, and Thorbjorn cut off his hand, and then Grettir's fingers opened, and Thorbjorn picked up the sword. Holding it with both hands, he struck Grettir's head, and the blow was so heavy that a piece was broken from the sword's edge.

When the others asked why he had done that since Grettir was already dead, Thorbjorn said, "I will do more." And striking again at Grettir's neck, he cut off his head.

"Now do I know that he is truly dead," said Thorbjorn. "We will take his head with us so that all men will know that it was I who slew Grettir and should have the money that was put upon it."

They told him he could do as he pleased, but it was clear that they thought he was behaving basely and they liked it not.

Then Thorbjorn spoke to Illugi and said, "It is a great pity that one so brave as you should have joined your fortune to that of this outlaw and followed him in his evil ways. For you see what it has led to for him and perhaps for you, too."

"It led to death for Grettir and it may be it will mean my death, too," said Illugi. "But when the All-Thing meets next summer it shall be seen whether this will end the matter for you and that witch, your foster mother. For it was her spells that undid him. And though you killed him in the end, it was when he was already at death's door."

"Those are bitter words you speak," said Thorbjorn. "But I will show you how I honor you by sparing your life if you will swear to take no vengeance on me or any who came here with me."

"That I will never do," said Illugi. "I might have agreed to it if Grettir had been able to defend himself and you had killed him in fair and equal combat. But if you let me live, I will never forget how you dealt with him, and sooner or later I shall avenge him."

Then Thorbjorn Angle talked with his fellows and asked what they thought he should do. But they would not give him an answer, saying that since he was their leader, he should decide this himself. And Thorbjorn said it would be madness to let a man live who had sworn to have his life.

When Illugi knew they meant to kill him, he laughed and said, "For this much I thank you, Thorbjorn. For you are doing that which I hoped you would do."

It was now late and dark, and they were worn out with fighting, so they rested through the night, taking turns keeping watch. But when dawn came, they led Illugi to the eastern part of the island, and there they slew him. Afterwards all said that there had never been one so young who had carried himself so bravely. Then they laid Grettir by his side and raised a cairn over both of them. But Thorbjorn took Grettir's head and his sword with him when they left the island, and they also took Glaum. Glaum never came alive to land, however. For, living up to his name, he kept complaining and protesting so noisily that, in disgust at his behavior and his betrayal of his trust, they killed him, too.

So died Grettir who had helped others in their hour of need, but who, in his own darkest hour, had only his brother to stand with him, and that was both their deaths. Grettir was thirty-five years old when he died, and Illugi was eighteen. And though Grettir had been an outlaw for almost twenty years, there were few who did not mourn his passing and say that he had been, not only the strongest, but the bravest man who ever dwelled in Iceland.

27

The Avenging of Grettir

THE tale is not yet ended. When Thorbjorn Angle returned from Drangey, he laid Grettir's head in salt and put it in an outbuilding to preserve it. Shortly after Yule, he went to see Thorir of Gard. He told him of the slaying of Grettir and said he had come for the money that had been offered as a reward for his death.

"No one has suffered more at Grettir's hands than I," said Thorir. "For it was because of him that my two sons were burned to death in Norway. But I would never have taken his life as you have done, when he was already dying because of your foster mother's witchcraft. I will not pay you the money since it seems to me that you are a far greater evil doer than Grettir ever was."

"That sounds most honorable and pious," said Thorbjorn. "But I think that there is something else behind
it. I think you care more about the money than you
do about the way in which I killed Grettir."

"There is an easy way to settle the matter," said
Thorir. "All we need do is wait for the All-Thing
and let the Lawman decide what is right."

Thorir would say nothing more to Thorbjorn. And
when Thorbjorn rode home, there was not only ill
will between him and Thorir, but it came to him that
if Thorir felt this way about the slaying of Grettir,
most of the other men would feel that way, too.
Nevertheless he was determined to press the matter
at the Thing.

Early in the summer Thorbjorn gathered together
some twenty men and rode westward toward Bjarg.
When Grettir's mother, Asdis, heard of his coming,
she sent out a call to her kin and her friends, and they
were many. Not only that, but she was so well loved
that all in Midfjord said that they would stand with
her, even those who had once been Grettir's enemies.

Asdis was in the hall when Thorbjorn arrived at
Bjarg. Only a few of her menfolk were with her for
most of those who had promised her their support
had not yet arrived. Thorbjorn went into the hall
followed by his men, and in his hand he carried
Grettir's head.

"Greetings, mistress," he said. "You have by now

heard of the death of your sons. Illugi lies buried on Drangey where he met his end. But if you would have sight of Grettir once more, here he is." And he set the head down on the floor.

Asdis sat silent for a moment, looking at Grettir's head. Then she spoke a verse:

> *Long have I lived and much have I seen,*
> *Sights both strange and dread.*
> *But this I never thought to see: a swine*
> *Who walks in the guise of a man*
> *And carries a hero's head.*
> *No need for spells like Thurid's,*
> *Nor to put a curse on your name.*
> *For fare where you will in whatever land*
> *You shall still bear the brand of your shame.*

All said afterward that none should be surprised that she should have had such brave sons when she herself had been so brave and had borne herself so well at that time. It had been in Thorbjorn's mind when he came to Bjarg to lay claim to all of Illugi's property because he had aided Grettir, who was an outlaw. But at that moment many men were seen riding toward the stead from the west, and these were the friends and supporters of Asdis. And when Thorbjorn saw who they were, he thought it best to hold his peace.

Thorbjorn and his men left the hall and, though

there were many among those who supported Asdis who wished to attack him, the older and wiser men bade them keep the peace and see how matters went at the All-Thing. Thus was Thorbjorn able to ride away, bearing Grettir's head with him. But he was even less happy now than when he left Thorir.

When Thorbjorn got ready to ride to the Thing, his party was smaller than he had thought it would be, for most men spoke ill of the way he had dealt with Grettir. He had meant to take Grettir's head with him, but his brother-in-law, Halldor, told him not to, saying, "The feeling against you is strong enough as it is without stirring up fresh anger and grief."

So Thorbjorn let him take Grettir's head and bury it in a sand hill, which from that time on was called Grettir's Hillock.

When Thorbjorn arrived at the Thing, matters were even worse for him than he had feared. He made his claim for the money that had been laid on Grettir's head, and Thorir answered as he had when Thorbjorn came to see him at Gard. Before the Lawman gave his opinion, he asked whether anyone had any counter charges to make which had any bearing on the matter. As Grettir's nearest of kin, Skeggi, the son of Gamli, came forward and presented two charges against Thorbjorn. The first was that Thorbjorn made use of witchcraft and sorcery and that it was through them that Grettir had met his death. And the second was that he had killed a man who was already dying, both being crimes which were punishable by outlawry.

There was a difference of opinion about the charges, but there were few who supported Thorbjorn and some who thought he should be punished by death, not outlawry. But in the end the sentence passed was that Thorbjorn should leave Iceland and not return while any who had been involved in the case on behalf of Grettir and Illugi should still live.

When Thorbjorn saw how the matter was going, he left the Thing, for he thought that Grettir's friends might attack him. He did not get the money that had been put on Grettir's head, and so he had nothing for his deed and his appearance at the Thing but exile and shame.

Thorbjorn sailed for Norway and, for a while, made much of himself. He told only that part of the story of the slaying of Grettir as did him credit and so made it out to have been a great deed. But those who knew Grettir thought there must be more to the tale than he told.

That autumn word of Grettir's death came to Thorsteinn Dromund, Grettir's half brother, in Tunsberg. He not only grieved at the news, but he also remembered the talk he had had with Grettir about his arms, which were not so mighty as Grettir's, but which he had told Grettir might one day avenge him. Thorbjorn was in the north at the time and Thorsteinn in the south, so they did not see one another during the winter. But Thorsteinn saw to it that word was sent to him of Thorbjorn's movements.

Thorbjorn for his part knew that Grettir had a brother in Norway, and it seemed to him that this might prove dangerous, so he sought counsel as to where he might go. At that time many Northmen were going to Micklegard to take service in the Varangian Guard of Michael Catalactus who was then king there. Thorbjorn thought he might do worse than go there where he could win both fame and fortune, and so he took ship and sailed south.

When Thorsteinn Dromund heard that Thorbjorn had left Norway, he turned over all his property to his kinsmen and took ship also, determined to follow Thorbjorn wherever he went and avenge his brother Grettir.

He, too, sailed south, past Denmark and along the narrow sea between England and the land of the Franks, past Spain and through the straits that lie between Spain and the country of the Moors. The water was warm and blue now, and strange fish that seemed to fly rose before the prow of the ship. Past many islands, large and small, sailed Thorsteinn, past Crete and the land of the Greeks and came at last to Micklegard that the men in those parts called Constantinople after an early Roman emperor who had ruled there.

It was a fair city, the greatest that Thorsteinn had ever seen, built on several hills and with the sea on three sides of it. He went to the place where the Varangians were quartered and said he wished to join them. Varangian, in the old language of the Northmen, means one

who has pledged himself to a leader. It was the name
by which the Slavs of Russia called the Vikings who
had invaded their country, and all those in the Varangian Guard were Northmen, for those in Micklegard
judged them the greatest warriors and the most trust-
worthy in the world. When Thorsteinn told those in

the Guard that he was from Norway and skilled in the use of weapons, they at once made him one of their number.

But now Thorsteinn faced a difficulty. He had never seen Thorbjorn Angle and so did not know him. He could not ask for him by name since this would be a warning to Thorbjorn, and besides he might have come into the Guard under a name that was not his own. So all Thorsteinn could do was watch and wait, and this was not easy. For there were many in the Varangian Guard and thus many to watch, and waiting comes hard when one is far from home and in a strange land.

And so days passed, there in that great city where the summer lingered far longer than it did in the north. There were many things to be seen: fair women and dark men from the East, the huge church of Saint Sophia with its high vaulted dome, and the hippodrome where men wagered all they possessed on the chariot races. But Thorsteinn paid little heed to any of these things. When he was not on duty, he spent all his time with others of the Guard, listening always to hear whether one of them would show himself to be Thorbjorn by even such a small thing as talk of Iceland. But though there were some Icelanders among the Varangians, they had been in Micklegard for some time and so could not be the man he sought.

There was one man whom Thorsteinn noticed because he kept to himself and spoke little to anyone. He was a big, strong, one-eyed man, very alert and watchful. But since his quarters were in another part of the barracks, it was not easy for Thorsteinn to fall into talk with him or any who shared his quarters.

One day, however, the Varangians were ordered to take the field against certain enemies of the king. But before they left, it was the custom to have a weapon show in which their arms were inspected to make sure that they were in order.

On the day appointed, Thorsteinn appeared with all the other Varangians for the weapon show. One of the first to have his arms inspected was the big, one-eyed man. He drew his sword and presented it to the captains, and as soon as Thorsteinn saw it unsheathed, he recognized it as the sword that Grettir had taken from the howe at Haramsey, and so he knew that this must be Thorbjorn.

When the captains examined the sword, they said that it was truly a noble blade and asked how it was that the blade was notched. By this time Thorbjorn had become less wary and more boastful.

"That," he said, "is a tale worth telling. There was a great hero in Iceland named Grettir the Strong. He had slain many men and was an outlaw for almost twenty years, but none could deal with him until I came upon him. Though he was the strongest man in the North, I overcame him in single combat. After I had killed him, I cut off his head with this, his own

sword, and in doing so, I broke this piece from the edge."

Those who were standing by said that Thorbjorn must be a great warrior to have slain such a champion, and that this Grettir must have had a hard skull. They passed the sword from hand to hand, admiring it.

"May I see it?" asked Thorsteinn.

"Wherefore not?" said Thorbjorn, handing it to him.

Thorsteinn looked at it closely, then nodded, saying, "Yes, this is indeed Grettir's sword."

"Did you doubt me?" asked Thorbjorn.

"No," said Thorsteinn. "But I wanted to make certain. Because, since it was Grettir's, it is only fitting that it be the blade that avenges him."

And heaving it high, he struck at Thorbjorn, and it was such a mighty blow that it clove his skull even to the jawbone and Thorbjorn fell down dead.

The captains at once ordered Thorsteinn to be seized and asked him why he had done such a thing. When Thorsteinn told them that he was Grettir's brother, many said that it was a great deed that he had done in coming so far to avenge his kin. But the elders of the town said that while the tale he told might be true, there was none to bear witness for him, and so they locked him in a dark dungeon and told him he must remain there until such time as he was ransomed.

For a time it looked as if the remainder of Thorsteinn's days were to be as dark as his cell. But he did not lose heart. Instead he sang to keep up his spirits, and he was such a singer that none in those parts had heard his like before. Since the prison was close to the street, many stopped to hear his singing, and among them was a rich and well-born lady of Micklegard named Spes. She fell into talk with him through the barred window of his cell, and his talk was so brave and high-spirited that she found herself in love with him and paid the ransom for his release. In time they were married, and their life together was long and so happy that Thorsteinn was accounted the most fortunate of men.

Thus did Thorsteinn's long journey end. And thus also ends the tale of Grettir who was one of Iceland's greatest heroes: a man who did many brave deeds, but lost his luck early in his life and, undone by witchcraft, was at last avenged in a foreign land far from home.

ABOUT THE AUTHOR

Robert Newman was born in New York City and was educated at the Ethical Culture School and Brown University. In addition to his adult novels, he has written several books for young people. The Icelandic sagas have always been a special interest of his. He lives in New York City with his wife, Dorothy Crayder, who is also a writer.

ABOUT THE ILLUSTRATOR

John Gretzer has spent much of his life in the Midwest. He was born in Council Bluffs, Iowa, attended the University of Omaha, and studied at the Kansas City Art Institute for a year under Thomas Hart Benton.

Mr. Gretzer has been active in the production of animated movies and in department-store advertising. He was at one time art director for a publishing firm and now undertakes free-lance assignments involving advertising and editorial art. He is the illustrator of several books for children.

Mr. Gretzer and his family live in Perkasie, Pennsylvania.